INTERNATIONAL TREATIES IN NATURE CONSERVATION: A UK PERSPECTIVE

DAVID A. STROUD, RUTH CROMIE,
MAX FINLAYSON, MELISSA LEWIS, TAEJ MUNDKUR,
DAVE PRITCHARD, CHRIS SPRAY, MARK TASKER,
NIALL TIERNEY, RACHEL TIERNEY AND JEREMY D. WILSON

Published by Biodiversity Press
An imprint of NHBS Ltd

NHBS Ltd
1–3 The Stables, Totnes, UK, TQ9 5LE
www.nhbs.com

First published in May 2021

A catalogue record for this book is available from the British Library

ISBN: 978-1-5272-8631-3 (paperback)

Design by Ian Atherton (corbiculadesign.co.uk)
Printed by Hobbs the Printers Ltd, Southampton, UK

1 2 3 4 5 6 7 8 9 10

Suggested citation:
Stroud, D. A., Cromie, R., Finlayson, M., Lewis, M., Mundkur, T., Pritchard, D., Spray, C., Tasker, M., Tierney, N., Tierney, R., & Wilson, J. D. 2021. *International treaties in nature conservation: a UK perspective.* Biodiversity Press, Totnes.

MIX
Paper from
responsible sources
FSC® C020438

Cover: photo by Gregory 'Slobirdr' Smith, licensed under CC BY-SA 2.0.
This image has been modified.

'With the goal of establishing a new and equitable global partnership through the creation of new levels of cooperation among States, key sectors of societies and people…

Working towards international agreements which respect the interests of all and protect the integrity of the global environmental and developmental system…

Recognizing the integral and interdependent nature of the Earth, our home…'

Preamble to the Rio Declaration on Environment and Development, 1992

Contents

Preface

Many environmental success stories of recent decades, including legislation to protect species, terrestrial and marine networks of protected areas, and prohibition of trade in endangered species, are the direct result of European Union (EU) or global international treaties. Yet, despite these achievements, the mechanisms of treaties remain poorly understood outside the world of international policy. In this work, we aim to shed light on the key features of these international processes in relation to nature conservation, especially in the UK, revealing how such treaties and institutions came about, how they function in theory and practice, the main issues they address and the challenges they face both in making decisions and in terms of their national and international implementation.

Multilateral Environmental Agreements (MEAs) provide essential and cost-effective means of addressing the many environmental issues created by humankind, although ultimately their effectiveness is limited by the extent to which they are implemented by their Contracting Parties (ratifying countries). This includes not only what those Parties do within their own territories but also what cooperative efforts they engage in across state borders. Where such cooperation is achieved it can establish shared, international frameworks for action, resulting in work over scales larger than those of individual nation-states. This can, for example, stimulate common approaches for surveillance and monitoring, which are vital for the development of national and international conservation priorities and verification of progress.

One of the crucial functions of MEAs is to provide a long view. Democracies worldwide are subject to re-election every few years, and this can result in rapid change of priorities and timescales for action. In contrast, MEAs focus on longer periods (and wider areas) and can thus offer perspectives that are resilient to short-term, national, political cycles.

Recent years have seen the explicit alignment of both human development and environmental protection agendas not just within the work of the Convention on Biological Diversity (CBD), but especially through the United Nations' (UN) Sustainable Development Goals (SDGs). This comes from recognition that degraded environments are both a cause and consequence of economic development challenges, and further have become drivers of global heating and changing climate. Indeed, international processes now typically recognise the complex linkages of human development with environmental and climate change crises, as exemplified by the UN's Intergovernmental Science-Policy Platform on Biodiversity and Ecosystem Services (IPBES). To that end, there is an urgent need for such interconnectedness to be translated into coherent national policies – including in the UK.

The UK's international influence with respect to nature conservation and environmental protection historically has been important and creditable. The UK has influenced EU nature conservation legislation and policy, and EU positions in those areas. Departure of the UK from the EU risks a major backwards step from a conservation perspective, especially regarding the removal of strong compliance mechanisms that hold government to the environmental obligations it has assumed.

However, there remains much room for improvement on certain matters, including, notably: the failure to address weak coordination across both UK government, and with and between the devolved administrations; establishment of consistent UK responses to different MEAs dealing with similar problems; and inconsistent engagement with the non-government sector. Many of these issues are long-standing.

Overall, the international landscape of MEAs created largely since the 1970s is profoundly enabling of national actions for nature conservation, wider environmental management and sustainable development. Nonetheless, the recent growth of nationalism and a consequent retreat from internationalism threatens to limit the effectiveness of international processes that are essential to addressing the world's biggest environmental threats.

1 Introduction

Those familiar with the conservation literature will be used to seeing the word 'international' in a wide range of contexts, such as 'internationally important', 'international proportion', 'international site', 'international legislation', 'international organisation' and many others besides. Throwing in the closely related terms 'European' and 'global', it is clear that international contexts are not only important for nature conservation but also have multiple scales.[1]

This review explores some of these issues,[2] especially the rarefied world of international environmental instruments,[3] with its COPs and MOPs (Conference, and Meeting, of the Parties respectively), Agreements and agreements (which are different things!), strategic plans and high-level targets. But what is a 'convention' and why do we need so many of them? What do they all do? Do they actually make a difference? Are they joined up? And crucially, how can governments and we, the public, use them to best effect?

---

1 'International' in this context means relating to more than one country, including bilateral, transboundary and regional cooperation systems, and to wildlife populations/natural resources that are shared by multiple (any number of) countries. 'International' can refer to global systems but is not restricted to that scale or context.

2 Much of what follows addresses those international mechanisms related to nature conservation. Yet, rightly, there is no sharp boundary around these, and other international mechanisms address wider environmental issues such as climate, water, chemical pollution and a host of others. We draw selective examples from this wider spectrum of treaties to illustrate particular points but provide no comprehensive review! We also note our largely European perspectives.

3 Although sometimes referred to as international 'legislation', this really is only accurate for EU laws, since conventions, agreements and protocols are not adopted by legislative bodies. We introduce here not only MEAs but also a range of other political structures and frameworks operating internationally that impact on nature conservation, collectively called international instruments.

People make policy and laws at geopolitical scales that do not match the biogeographical organisation of nature. In policy-making for nature, however, we must try to align them better. For the many ecological systems and species populations that straddle national boundaries (or lie beyond national jurisdictions), the only sensible scale at which to establish priorities and frameworks is the international scale.

These international processes are hugely important in establishing national priorities and frameworks for nature conservation, but they are far from perfect. Many international treaties are not focused solely on nature conservation; rather, they seek a balance between use or exploitation on the one hand, and conservation on the other (e.g. whaling; see Appendix 2). Further, the 'landscape' of international treaties and organisations described here, in particular their form, function and relationships, is messy. It has developed over half a century, creating its own approaches and norms, and exploiting opportunities provided by international political structures, such as the UN and the EU. It is the result of evolution rather than design, and the way that this is all currently organised is almost certainly not what one would plan on a blank piece of paper!

Yet, while imperfect, such structures are the best tools available to tackle some of the biggest environmental issues we face. Indeed, international processes allow us to understand and respond to the existential crisis of climate change as nations collectively grapple with the challenge of managing the ultimate common resource – the planet's atmosphere – although against a background of historical failure to address the fundamental causes of the problem, including over-population, over-consumption and deeply unsustainable lifestyles.

The COVID-19 pandemic provides an interesting contrast. As the virus spread in 2020 there was no agreed political frame for even an attempted shared approach, with instead an early retreat to national responses – despite the urgency of the issue and enormous international ramifications. In a 'globalised' world with massive interconnectivity, the World Health Organization (WHO) provides advisory notes only, and very different approaches have been implemented at national scales, with the USA briefly leaving the WHO altogether (before rejoining in January 2021). In contrast, the response of the scientific community – on research to underpin vaccine development – has been more internationalist, and the pandemic provides lessons that will need to be learned regarding the international collaboration required to reverse the biodiversity crisis and to halt climate change. Both these issues, explored below, are challenging in the extreme, and will require significant changes to multiple national policies with all the short-term, political stresses that will arise.

2 Establishing international contexts

The current generation of conservationists perhaps takes for granted international knowledge and perspectives. Yet, in the early development of international nature conservation policy, this understanding was hard-won against a background of significant communication difficulties. In the case of migratory waterbirds, for instance, a generation of conservation advocates with an international outlook started to communicate across Europe after the Second World War in order to share knowledge and understanding of avian movements and numbers. Pioneers such as Sir Peter Scott and Phyllis Barclay-Smith in the UK, Luc Hoffmann in France and Jan Rooth in the Netherlands established the International Wildfowl Research Bureau (IWRB)[4] in 1947, a small secretariat which then stimulated the International Waterbird Census – a coordinated midwinter count of as many European waterbodies as possible (Hindle 1964; Kuijken 2006; Boere 2010).

IWRB created a mechanism not just to develop the science but, through Luc Hoffmann's 1962 Project Mar (so-called because 'mar' is the root of many European words for wetland – marsh, marais, marécages etc.), created the first inventory of internationally important wetlands across the continent (Hoffmann 1964; Olney 1965) and lobbied for an intergovernmental

---

4 Historically having had multiple names (Kuijken 2006), currently Wetlands International.

agreement on wetland conservation – which was finalised in 1971 at the Iranian city of Ramsar (Matthews 1993).

At about the same time as Project Mar, the concept of a pan-European flora was raised at the 8th International Congress of Botany in 1954, with *Flora Europaea* progressively published from 1964 to provide a continent-scale summary of European plant distributions – critical for later exercises in conservation prioritisation. Context-setting continues, with the progressive growth of knowledge from the scale of individual species and habitats to those of global systems.

Such international context-setting necessarily involved developing and harmonising methods, terminologies and standards to aid greater commonality of approaches, along with interchangeability of knowledge across national borders. Common across all such exercises was an initial drive from the science community, facilitated by groups of specialists.[5] Indeed, there are multiple examples where citizens and enthusiasts, rather than larger organisations, have stimulated important international initiatives.

The growth of internationally shared knowledge was greatly assisted by the creation both of the UN's agencies and programmes (notably the UN Educational, Scientific and Cultural Organization [UNESCO] in 1945, and in 1972 the UN Environment Programme [UNEP]),[6] as well as the International Union for the Conservation of Nature (IUCN), one of whose explicit objectives in 1948 was to 'collect, analyse, interpret and

Project Mar collated the first pan-European assessment of internationally important wetlands, shown here as black dots. From Olney (1965).

---

5 One example is the International Wader Study Group's first assessment of wader population sizes across Europe (Piersma 1986).

6 While education, science, culture, health, food and agriculture all got dedicated UN organisations, environment belatedly received a 'programme' in 1972, a significantly lower-status response.

Large areas of the naturally treeless Flow Country in northern Scotland were ecologically devastated by drainage and planting with non-native conifers in the 1980s, encouraged by tax incentives. In recent years, and supported by international funding from the EU's LIFE (L'Instrument Financier pour l'Environnement) programme, much restoration has occurred – most trees in this image have now been felled. Recognition of the critical importance of peatlands for biodiversity and for carbon and water management continues to grow, considering in particular their extent, condition and need for restoration. Peatlands are significantly represented in the UK, with the Flow Country currently being considered for World Heritage Site status.

disseminate information about "the protection of nature"' (see p. 21 and Holdgate 1999).

Such science-based developments were overlaid by other changes taking place in the same period. The Second World War defined a new international context in three respects: (i) technological advances in connectivity (for example, radio and long-range aerial bombers); (ii) highlighting interdependences (such as North Atlantic alliances and the dependency of Europe on food imported from other continents);[7] and (iii) post-war multilateralist idealism – notably the Atlantic Charter, the European Project and development of novel global political and financial frameworks such as the UN and the USA-driven Bretton Woods system of the World Bank, International Monetary Fund and International Bank for Reconstruction and Development.

Although on the North American continent there had been important early development of international conservation treaties (Dorsey 1998) for the shared management of economically important wildlife, especially fisheries, modern international conservation treaties, contexts and organisations were very much products of post-war goals and aspirations.

---

7   Although the core function of empires in providing resources to the centre goes back millennia.

Setting of international contexts can be of critical importance for national conservation. For example, in 1987 the Nature Conservancy Council (NCC) made a high-profile case to government for the protection of peatlands in northern Scotland from afforestation. Stroud *et al.* (2015) subsequently explained the crucial significance of establishing the international context of the Flow Country, so allowing the NCC to state: 'This is possibly the largest single expanse of blanket bog in the world and the largest single area of habitat in the United Kingdom that is of major importance on the world scale because of its global scarcity' (Stroud *et al.* 1987).

Global assessment processes

A fundamental form of international cooperation on the environment comes from the means and desire to share knowledge and data, which have progressively resulted in the ability to undertake assessments of the state of the planet. There is a long history of such scientific cooperation (for instance, the four International Polar Years since 1882, and the creation of the International Council for the Exploration of the Sea in 1902 for the collection and international sharing of data on marine ecosystems). In recent years, however, the international community has developed several formal assessment processes explicitly to inform the development of international policy.

Left. The comprehensive IPBES assessment on Biodiversity and Ecosystem Services gave these issues a new degree of worldwide attention with its 'Summary for Policymakers' published in May 2019. Right. The final text was agreed line by line during an 18-hour session. Such negotiations are undertaken in English giving significant advantage to anglophones.

Table 1. Recent global assessments relevant to the UK. All sources are listed in the references.

Publication date	Assessment	Responsible organisation
2012	Waterbird Population Estimates, 5th edition	Wetlands International
2014	Climate Change 2014: Fifth Assessment Report	IPCC
2014	Global Biodiversity Outlook (GBO) 4	CBD
2015	European Environment – State and Outlook 2015: Assessment of Global Megatrends Synthesis Report	European Environment Agency (EEA)
2017	Pollinators, Pollination and Food Production	IPBES
2017	Global Land Outlook	UN Convention to Combat Desertification
2018	Land Degradation and Restoration	IPBES
2018	Special Report: Global Warming of 1.5°C	IPCC
2018	Global Wetland Outlook	Ramsar Convention
2019	Biodiversity and Ecosystem Services	IPBES
2019	Global Environment Outlook (GEO) 6	UNEP
2020	State of World Fisheries and Aquaculture*	UN Food and Agriculture Organization (FAO)
2020	World Water Development Report*	UNESCO
2020	State of the World's Forests	FAO
2020	GBO 5	CBD
2020	Mapping and Assessment of Ecosystems and their Services	EU
2020	State of nature in the EU	EU

*Published annually.

The role of the Intergovernmental Panel on Climate Change (IPCC) is well known. It was established in 1988 by the World Meteorological Organization and UNEP (with later endorsement from the UN General Assembly) with the objective of providing scientific information on the risks of human-induced global warming and possible response options.

In 2012, IPBES (also supported by UNEP) was established to undertake essentially similar functions for biodiversity.

None of these assessments could have been produced without the worldwide voluntary inputs of thousands of scientists (both professional and 'citizen') and their organisations and universities. In considering governmental processes below, it is important not to forget such vital *pro bono* contributions.

Recent assessment reports produced by IPCC, IPBES and others (Table 1) have played a huge role in raising the profile of international environmental issues – we return to their conclusions at the end.

Many humans have profoundly unsustainable lifestyles with national economies based on continual consumption, which is now resulting in planetary-scale consequences. It is increasingly recognised internationally that addressing this is the ultimate challenge. Manila, Philippines, 2017.

The current state of the planet

Prior to the turn of the millennium, governments themselves rarely, if ever, formally discussed the root causes (sometimes called primary drivers) of environmental degradation: there was usually a herd of environmental 'elephants in the room'. Thus, formal Resolutions would refer to habitat loss but rarely expand on its root causes, let alone discuss how those drivers of disruption should be addressed. More recently, and especially following the involvement of the academic community in assessment processes, the situation is now more honest. Hence, UNEP's *GEO 5* in 2012 remarked:

The EEA's 11 global megatrends include: growing pressure on ecosystems; increasing environmental pollution; increasingly severe consequences of climate change; changing disease burden and risks of pandemics; and intensified global competition for resources.

THE EUROPEAN ENVIRONMENT
STATE AND OUTLOOK 2015
ASSESSMENT OF GLOBAL MEGATRENDS

'*There are compelling reasons to consider policies and programmes that focus on the underlying drivers that contribute to increased pressure on environmental conditions, rather than concentrating only on reducing environmental pressures or symptoms. Drivers include, inter alia, the negative aspects of population growth, consumption and production, urbanization and globalization.*'

Now, all recent global assessments agree on a nexus of three issues:[8]

1. a climate emergency
2. a global ecological crisis
3. an imperative to address human development issues.

---

8   The extent to which the underlying driver of population growth is addressed tends to vary in different contexts. Typical is the IPBES global assessment (IPBES 2019), which acknowledges population growth but skirts round the detail: 'In the past 50 years, the human population has doubled, the global economy has grown nearly fourfold and global trade has grown tenfold, together driving up the demand for energy and materials.'

It is ultimately not possible to address one of these problems without also addressing the other two since they are interlinked with often mutual solutions; initiatives such as the UN's SDGs now recognise this.

At a more detailed level, several common and connected themes have emerged (see Box A), none of which will come as a surprise to those aware of environmental issues. Some are considered by the EEA (2015) as global 'megatrends'.

Box A. Environmental problems highlighted by multiple international assessments

These include, in no particular order:

- poor land management (especially of soils, wetlands and forests) with consequences for carbon emissions, food production and biodiversity loss;
- over-consumption and the fundamental problem of continued encouragement to consume as the basis of the economy;
- interactions between a growing global population, over-consumption, and the implications for food and resources of bringing increasingly large numbers of people out of poverty through development;
- international movement and migrations of people across the globe, including environmental refugees;
- corruption and poor governance as an impediment to national implementation of crucial measures;

Deforestation and poor management of soils, especially from over-grazing (as shown here in Uzbekistan, in 2003), have severely reduced both biodiversity and the scope for food production in many parts of the world.

Environmental degradation is both a cause and consequence of human development challenges, linked, for example, to sanitation problems and the associated transmission of disease. Madagascar.

- consequences of increasing globalisation of trade and travel for continued spread of alien invasive species and pathogens, including potential further pandemic risk;
- illegal and unsustainable capture, killing and trade of wildlife;
- implications of growing urbanisation;
- increasing concentration of resources in the hands of a few;
- unsustainable management of marine resources;[9]
- the existential challenge of developing processes to manage the atmosphere as the ultimate global commons.

So, with the context of interconnected global threats accepted and a certain ability to cooperate between nations, what is required is for countries to agree necessary actions.

A rapidly growing proportion of the world population lives, or will live, in urban areas. This has implications for all aspects of the natural environment. United Arab Emirates.

9   In 2004, the UN General Assembly launched negotiations on a new international legally binding instrument under the UN Convention on the Law of the Seas (UNCLOS) to regulate and sustainably use marine biodiversity beyond national jurisdictions: the Biodiversity Beyond National Jurisdiction process. As of 2021, this is at a draft text stage and may ultimately lead to a new High Seas Treaty.

3 International treaties: what are they and what do they do?

International cooperation for nature conservation takes many forms. The first to arise historically, and also the simplest, is individual scientists working together and exchanging information on issues of joint interest and concern. This can lead to shared working by organisations (such as through information exchange and the transfer of resources and skills), as in many joint research programmes, and then further development via bilateral cooperation between countries at a governmental level. Examples include formal twinning programmes between nature reserves, involving exchanges of staff and expertise.

Developing such cooperation further can result in bilateral treaties between countries. For example, in 1916 a convention for the protection of migratory birds was bilaterally agreed between the USA and the UK (on behalf of Canada).[10] This remains in force and, following a further treaty with Mexico in 1936, has been fundamental in driving bird conservation across North America (Dorsey 1998; Boardman 2006). Not all proposed treaties reach fruition, however. For instance, the UK was well advanced in negotiations for a bilateral treaty on the conservation of migratory waterbirds with the USSR – until that country's invasion of Afghanistan in 1979 brought the process to a halt.

---

10 Under the Canadian Constitution Act of 1867, the UK retained control of Canada's foreign affairs. Canada only achieved full sovereignty in 1982.

Due to the complexities of dealing with multiple separate bilateral agreements, it has been more typical in recent decades for governments to develop multilateral environment treaties, or MEAs, instead.[11]

Reasons to work together internationally

Governments agree to work together at international scales essentially for two reasons.[12]

The first is to address issues larger than the nation-state. Thus, the CBD establishes a global framework for national and international policies related to genetic, species and ecosystem conservation, while, more specifically, the African-Eurasian Waterbird Agreement (AEWA) creates a common framework for conservation and management of migratory waterbirds and their habitats across their vast flyways and the even greater extent of the AEWA area. Some frameworks relate to the need to manage environmental resources shared internationally between nation-states. Good examples are the establishment of

A good example of bilateral international cooperation is the current use of Norwegian landscapes (with natural tree lines) as a reference for the monitoring and research programmes in the Cairngorms, Scotland. Cooperation between the Cairngorms Connect partnership and the Norwegian Institute for Nature Research is exploring landscape changes that could occur as forests expand towards their natural limits, as here in Invereshie at about 650m. Naturally regenerated areas in south-west Norway, climatically similar to Scotland, allow comparison of habitats and species between countries.

11 See **Further reading and resources** for more sources of information on MEAs.

12 An alternative view, from a political science perspective, suggests that treaty development is not just about environmental challenges and global concern, but also about power relations and geopolitics (Mitchell 2010). This sees MEAs as a way of embedding neoliberal institutions into the international system, or challenging current forms of global power (see Paterson et al. 2003). However, at least for Ramsar, AEWA and several other Convention on Migratory Species (CMS) agreements, no such thinking is apparent in accounts (or from personal knowledge) of their genesis (Matthews 1993; Boere 2010), so this is probably post-hoc rationalisation in terms of the motives, even if it correctly identifies a resulting outcome.

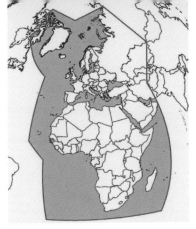

The AEWA area encompasses the total extent of migratory flyway systems of all migratory waterbirds occurring within it.

national quotas for the shooting of migratory waterbirds that fly between multiple countries during their annual cycle (such as in North America – see Schmidt 2006). This has been associated with academic collaboration over the development of methods to determine those quotas using Adaptive Harvest Management (AHM)[13] approaches.

Those examples relate to international agreements between States concerning what happens across their respective sovereign territories. Other agreements are made between States regarding what happens in areas beyond their territorial jurisdictions. Good examples of these relate to the harvest of resources that occur beyond individual States (see Appendix 2 for the example of whales; Wolf 1997).

The second motivation is related, but slightly different, in that it recognises that a common framework for action benefits all nations collectively. This 'common heritage' motivation[14] is very well expressed in the Preamble to the Ramsar Convention (Box B).

The scale at which nations come together to collaborate varies. Some treaties have global reach, while others are of regional scope. The former are essential for addressing certain types of widespread environmental threat. The latter, however, often achieve more detailed and stringent commitments because they are negotiated among a smaller number of States (which may have similar cultures or be in similar states of development) and (sometimes) have a more restricted subject matter of direct national importance. This

---

13 AHM is a formal approach to managing limits to hunting, so as to ensure that harvests are sustainable. Accordingly, AHM responds to multiple sources of environmental and population uncertainty and, as for other forms of management, depends on monitoring and assessment. These thresholds are regularly revised in light of the most recent evaluations of population size and production. Setting of fisheries quotas should – in theory – be a form of AHM, although in many contexts (such as in the EU's Common Fisheries Policy) adaptive quota setting based on science is overlain by subsequent political interventions.

14 This is expressed quite explicitly in the wording of the World Heritage Convention (WHC) (negotiated in the 1960s and adopted in 1972), which refers to the 'heritage of all the nations of the world' and things that 'need to be preserved as part of the world heritage of mankind as a whole'.

UNCLOS, which defines the rights and responsibilities of nations with respect to their use of the world's oceans, also expresses the concept of common heritage. Negotiations in the 1960s included this concept and so it was embedded in the 1982 Convention. The subsequent 1994 agreement includes in its preamble: 'Reaffirming that the seabed and ocean floor and subsoil thereof, beyond the limits of national jurisdiction (hereinafter referred to as the 'Area'), as well as the resources of the Area, are the common heritage of mankind.' Yet, in contrast, the drafters of the CBD deliberately shied away from using the term 'common heritage', instead introducing the phrase 'common *concern* of humankind'.

Box B. Preamble to the Convention on Wetlands

The preamble to the Ramsar Convention explains that the agreement is made with the Contracting Parties:

'**Recognizing** the interdependence of Man and his environment;

Considering the fundamental ecological functions of wetlands as regulators of water regimes and as habitats supporting a characteristic flora and fauna, especially waterfowl;

Being convinced that wetlands constitute a resource of great economic, cultural, scientific, and recreational value, the loss of which would be irreparable;

Desiring to stem the progressive encroachment on and loss of wetlands now and in the future;

Being confident that the conservation of wetlands and their flora and fauna can be ensured by combining far-sighted national policies with co-ordinated international action;'

also results in objectives being easier to monitor, so aiding Parties to identify and realise the benefits of cooperation. Good examples are the various subject-limited Agreements of the Convention on Migratory Species (CMS) as compared to the global Convention itself.

These two scales are not mutually exclusive and can work together to complement or influence each other. The Southern African Development Community Protocol on Shared Watercourses, for instance, was based almost entirely on the UN Watercourses Convention but ended up coming into force before the global Convention.[15]

There are many kinds of international instrument too,[16] but in Europe there are essentially four broad types: the EU legislation; intergovernmental Conventions; legally non-binding instruments such as Action Plans; and a range of other structures such as formal international Partnerships. The differences between these and how they work are explained in Appendix 1.

Sovereignty

All Conventions necessarily result in a loss of 'sovereignty' through a nation's agreement to give up certain rights in exchange for achieving a shared objective. As an example, a nation's right to manufacture and trade ozone-depleting chlorofluorocarbons is given up in the interests of protecting the

---

15 After negotiation and signature, treaties undergo a process through which they either come into force (for legally binding instruments) or come into effect (for non-binding ones). This has two aspects. First, when the treaty itself comes into force/effect generally (through gaining a specified number or ratifications/accessions); and second, when it comes into force/effect for any given Party (some specified time after that Party's ratification/accession). Some Conventions do not come into force until many years after their original adoption.

16 Although it is common to talk of 'international treaties' in such a context, neither the EU Directives nor the soft law instruments adopted by COPs/MOPs technically constitute 'treaties' as defined by the legally overarching Vienna Convention on the Law of Treaties (1969). Further, although this book uses the term 'Convention' interchangeably with 'treaty', some treaties are framed as Agreements or Protocols (see Appendix 1).

ozone layer. (An alternative view is that this represents not 'loss' of sovereignty but an agreement *in line with* a country's sovereign rights to forgo some activity – in this example protecting a common resource in the common good that no single nation controls.)

What issues do treaties address?

Just about every aspect of environmental management is now informed by MEAs, and much – in theory at least – is regulated.

Some treaties are tightly focused on a specific problem. Maybe the best example is the 1987 Montreal Protocol, which responded to observed thinning of ozone in the upper atmosphere and a rapid diagnosis of the causes and consequences. International cooperation to regulate and phase out known ozone-depleting substances has been (until recently) highly effective (DeSombre 2000; UN Environment 2019).[17]

Other agreements have an exceptionally broad remit. For example, the CBD was the first treaty explicitly to address all aspects of biodiversity, but the consequent trade-off is that many of its provisions are broadly framed and heavily qualified in terms of their lack of firm commitments (see below).

Yet others concern the needs of certain taxonomic groups (e.g. whales, bats, albatrosses, migratory waterbirds), sometimes just within a defined area (e.g. small cetaceans in the Baltic and North Seas). Many seek to establish regulatory structures for action for major issues of environmental concern (e.g. wetlands, trade in endangered species, biodiversity, transboundary air pollution).

The recent focus of many MEAs (especially those that have global scope) has been to deliver their objectives within the context of sustainable development needs, as outlined in Box C.

Several common themes repeatedly occur across different international instruments. Focusing especially on the biodiversity-related MEAs (and their COP/MOP decisions and guidelines), rather than those addressing wider environmental problems, such issues include the need to:

- establish networks of well-managed protected areas (e.g. Ramsar, Bern,[18] the EU Nature Directives,[19] CBD);
- regulate trade in wildlife and its products to ensure sustainability (e.g. Bern, EU Nature Directives, Convention on International Trade in Endangered Species of Wild Fauna and Flora [CITES]);

---

17 However, many of the substitutes for ozone-depleting chemicals are now increasingly of concern. Hence, the initial target may have been reached, but the overall purpose has still to be achieved.

18 The Council of Europe's Bern Convention on the Conservation of European Wildlife and Natural Habitats (1979).

19 The EU's 1979 Bird Directive and 1992 Habitats Directive are sometimes jointly called the EU Nature Directives.

Box C. Sustainable development

The relationship between human development issues and biodiversity loss has become increasingly obvious. Throughout the world, degraded natural environments are both a cause and a consequence of poverty.

The 1972 UN Conference on the Human Environment in Stockholm was arguably the first global forum to address environmental aspects of development. Considered afresh, the 26 principles of the Stockholm Declaration[20] are remarkably farsighted, and to some extent we are simply reinventing them today. For example, Principle 11:

'The environmental policies of all States should enhance and not adversely affect the present or future development potential of developing countries, nor should they hamper the attainment of better living conditions for all, and appropriate steps should be taken by States and international organizations with a view to reaching agreement on meeting the possible national and international economic consequences resulting from the application of environmental measures.'

Yet while the 1980 Commission on International Development Issues (Brandt 1980) gave little attention to the environment per se, these concerns came increasingly to the fore through the work of the subsequent Brundtland Commission (World Commission on Environment and Development 1987), which prepared the way for the convening of the 1992 Earth Summit in Rio de Janeiro. That meeting adopted the Agenda 21 framework – and the Rio Declaration – and established the Commission on Sustainable Development. All these initiatives in turn started to slowly influence the operational procedures of the World Bank, whose previous funding of development projects often had major adverse environmental consequences (and remains problematic in many respects).

The 'three-legged stool' model of sustainable development has sustainability supported by the three legs of economy, social equity and the environment. Yet from the outset many saw the stool as distinctly unbalanced – with trade-offs typically being at the expense of the environment rather than the economy or human development needs, and with emphasis given to development at the expense of inconvenient environmental sustainability.

In 2000, the UN Millennium Declaration committed world leaders to combat poverty, hunger, disease, illiteracy, environmental degradation and discrimination against women. Eight Millennium Development Goals (MDGs) derived from this Declaration, each with specific targets and indicators. These helped steer international development activities to 2015.

Building on these MDGs, a follow-up process devised more comprehensive SDGs (UN General Assembly 2015) which draw out the intimate (and by now long recognised) linkages between environmental sustainability and human development. Indeed, there is intentional and significant overlap between adopted global biodiversity targets[21] and the SDGs.[22]

---

20 www.ipcc.ch/apps/njlite/srex/njlite_download.php?id=6471

21 Global biodiversity targets derive from the *The Strategic Plan for Biodiversity 2011–2020 and the Aichi Biodiversity Targets* (CBD 2010a) (see Table 3). While negotiated through CBD, the Plan was designed for the whole global biodiversity community and has been endorsed by other Conventions. As outlined below, the Aichi Targets ran to 2020 and will be superseded, with current negotiation of a new set of targets happening in the draft (and as of January 2021 indicatively named) 'Post-2020 Global Biodiversity Framework'.

22 Allan (2020) explores the links between MEAs and SDGs.

SDGs address the full range of human development needs including those related to gender. Female empowerment is critical to development throughout the world. SDG Target 5c requires actions to 'Adopt and strengthen sound policies and enforceable legislation for the promotion of gender equality and the empowerment of all women and girls at all levels.' Such international targets support the work of the global agency UN Women and many other organisations with gender equity objectives. Ghana, 2012.

There has also been a paradigm shift over this period, from carrying out development in ways that do not jeopardise other sets of values, to seeking to maintain those natural resources and support systems that make development possible. To give just one example, this shift is interestingly reflected in the successive revisions of the Ramsar Convention's fundamental definitions of 'wise use' and 'ecological character' (Pritchard 2016a,b).[23]

The sustainable development agenda now drives much of the UK government's international work. Thus, all the funding for the government's Darwin Initiative comes from Official Development Assistance (ODA) funds. Unfortunately, though, this has negative consequences for projects that solely have nature conservation objectives and it restricts the list of eligible countries – an outcome that renders the environment a junior partner to development.

---

23 At the outset of the Convention, maintenance of wetland 'ecological character' applied only to designated Ramsar Sites, while wise use was defined as 'the maintenance of their ecological character, achieved through the implementation of ecosystem approaches, within the context of sustainable development'. In 2005, however, the Convention recognised that the concept of ecological character is the key mechanism through which to achieve the wise use of *all* wetlands, and so redefined the earlier definition of wetland ecological character to: 'the combination of the ecosystem components, processes and benefits/services that characterise the wetland at a given point in time'. This emphasises wetland values much more strongly, although the term 'ecosystem services' was sensitive to some parties, hence the 'benefits/services' formulation.

- protect specific threatened taxa from disturbance, exploitation (deliberate or otherwise – for example through bycatch) or other threats (e.g. Bern, EU Nature Directives, CMS, AEWA, Agreement for the Conservation of Albatrosses and Petrels [ACAP] and other CMS Agreements);
- ensure any taking of live or dead animals conforms with high welfare standards through the prohibition of indiscriminate and unselective methods (e.g. Bern, EU Nature Directives, AEWA);

Most MEAs stress the critical need for education and raising public awareness.

The need to avoid poisoning wildlife through unsafe use of pesticides is a current priority for several MEAs, including CMS, AEWA, Memorandum of Understanding on the Conservation of Migratory Birds of Prey in Africa and Eurasia (Raptors MoU) and the EU Birds Directive. Ghana.

- sustainably manage the exploitation of resources on an adaptive basis involving monitoring and reporting of harvests and quota setting (e.g. International Whaling Commission [IWC; see Appendix 2], Regional Fisheries Management Organisations [RFMOs] and other fisheries agreements, EU Birds Directive, AEWA);
- prevent damage to, or loss of, an important resource, such as wetlands or ozone (e.g. Ramsar, Montreal Protocol);
- promote research, monitoring, and information-sharing (nearly all);
- rehabilitate and restore degraded ecosystems and promote recovery of threatened species (CBD, AEWA, ACAP, CMS, EU Nature Directives);
- prevent the introduction of (and control already-introduced) non-native, invasive species (and pathogens) that pose a threat to indigenous biodiversity (EU Nature Directives and Non-native Species Directive, AEWA, ACAP, CBD);[24]
- require environmental impact assessments for activities that have the potential significantly to affect biodiversity (and ensure that these processes incorporate public participation) (Ramsar, Bern, CMS, EU Nature Directives);
- raise awareness and strengthen capacity (either implicitly or, in many cases, explicitly);
- cooperate with other countries on shared resources or problems (all).[25]

---

24 The critical challenge of preventing the spread of invasive alien species, and their control or eradication, is addressed through a large number of international processes, including decisions by the relevant MEAs. IUCN's Invasive Species Specialist Group (www.issg.org) is a fine example of an international network of experts exchanging best practice information on multiple aspects of this issue in support of national and international processes.

25 A number of examples are given through this review, but a typical problem was the need to respond urgently to implications of the spread of Highly Pathogenic Avian Influenza (HPAI) H5N1 in the 2000s. This led to the establishment of a Scientific Task Force on Avian Influenza and Migratory Birds, which brought together countries, multiple MEAs and UN agencies, and facilitated the development of common messages, agendas, complementary Resolutions and common guidance (Cromie et al. 2011).

4 Historical development

The first substantive international conservation initiatives and Conventions were related to birds, with a number of international conferences on bird preservation in the last years of the nineteenth century, leading to the agreement of a 1902 Convention for the Protection of Birds Useful to Agriculture.[26] The history of this Convention provides an early example of how the initial proposed objectives of such treaties have often been undermined (Ferrero-García 2013). The draft text proposed legal protection for *all* bird species (with the exception of specified pest species), yet in order to accommodate Switzerland,[27] this was changed in the final version to give protection just to a short list of named species, thus missing an opportunity to create a pan-European bird protection regime 50 years earlier than eventually occurred. This is a reminder that most Conventions represent an uneasy compromise between what is environmentally desirable and what is politically possible.

In terms of wildlife preservation, however, the first international treaty was the North Pacific Fur Seal Convention of 1911, signed by the USA, the UK

---

26 The Convention involved 12 countries but not the UK. The genesis of the Convention and the watering down of its provisions are described by Ferrero-García (2013).

27 The 'restructuring of Article 5 was the result of a demand by Switzerland, precisely to prevent that Article from protecting many wild birds generically. Hence in 1899 the French Executive, despite initial opposition mainly from Austria-Hungary and Germany, pointed out the need to accept this imposition so as to prevent Switzerland from refusing to sign the treaty; its absence would have led, according to France, to the failure of the whole process' (Ferrero-García (2013).

(representing Canada), Japan and Russia, and which responded to the catastrophic overexploitation of northern fur seals (*Callorhinus ursinus*) and sea otters (*Enhydra lutris*) (Dorsey 1998).

At the governmental level, initiatives to create formal structures for international nature conservation stuttered through the first half of the twentieth century, with the baton being passed from the USA to the Netherlands, and then to Switzerland as World Wars and the Spanish flu pandemic intervened, and as key players (what we would now call 'conservation leaders' or 'influencers') either died or left positions of influence (well described by Holdgate 1999).

Role of the IUCN

In the history of international nature conservation, the massively influential role of the IUCN has a special place. This unique body was founded in 1948 as a union of governments, their national agencies, and non-government organisations (Holdgate 1999). Long before the general globalisation of communications, it provided an institutional framework specifically for networking and information exchange – and, critically, giving a non-political 'safe space' for government representatives to informally discuss the need for possible binding treaties. The roots of many treaties such as Ramsar and CBD lie deep in IUCN initiatives such as Project Mar and the *World Conservation Strategy* (1980), while IUCN's Red Data Books have provided an agreed international approach to describing species extinction risk and thus helping to prioritise conservation actions (Mace *et al.* 2008). The *World Conservation Strategy* and *Strategy for Sustainable Living* (1991), while not binding on governments, had considerable influence in creating a good direction of travel which was then developed more formally by CBD and others.

The United Nations

The UN has had an important environmental role. While initiatives such as the 1982 World Charter for Nature may have been more symbolic than an actual driver of policy,[28] the establishment and work of some of the UN's key bodies has been critical.

UNESCO traces its roots back to the League of Nations in 1921, but the current organisation was established in 1945 following considerable UK advocacy. UNESCO played a major role in facilitating both the establishment of IUCN in 1948, as well as the 1972 World Heritage Convention (WHC) –

---

28 Although the Charter's language, in relation to the moral imperative to respect other life forms, was very significant at the time.

which brought together the twin concepts of natural and cultural heritage.[29] However, in political terms the UK has had (and continues to have) a troubled relationship with UNESCO.[30]

The more recent UNEP was an outcome of the 1972 Stockholm Conference (see Box C and below) and has played a key role as the international body that functionally oversees many UN Conventions (such as CBD and the Climate Change Convention). UNEP now reports to the more recently established (2012) UN Environment Assembly (UNEA), the world's highest-level decision-making body on the environment, with membership of all 193 UN Member States. UNEA meets biennially to set priorities for global environmental policies and develop international environmental law.

The UN Development Programme (UNDP) has a major impact, increasingly positive, on the environment and species conservation at national and international level. More recently still, the agreement by the UN General Assembly in 2015 of the SDGs (building on the earlier MDGs) has been profoundly important in embedding issues of environmental sustainability within human development (see Box A).

While the UN spends significantly on the environment, UNEP's US$0.6 billion (bn) budget (in 2016) does not approach other areas of spending, such as $5.4bn for the World Food Programme and $8.9bn for peacekeeping operations.

Progressive development of treaties

Ocean-related treaties with a focus on pollution from shipping (especially oil pollution, which is particularly visible to the public) first appeared in the 1950s,[31] but the pace of development of international environmental instruments really picked up through an intense period from the early 1970s to the mid-1990s (Table 2). This came from the growing, and increasingly articulated, appreciation of international dimensions to what was even then being described as an environmental crisis (Nicholson 1970; Dasmann 1972). The advocacy of newly established non-governmental organisations (NGOs) with global recognition and perspective, such as Greenpeace and Friends of the Earth, both responded to and stimulated public pressure (Zelco 2013).

At governmental levels, progress was energised by the 1972 UN Stockholm Conference on the Human Environment (see Box C) which called specifically

---

29 The UK currently has five 'natural' World Heritage Sites: Dorset and East Devon Coast (England); Giant's Causeway and Causeway Coast (Northern Ireland); Gough and Inaccessible Islands (Tristan da Cunha); Henderson Island (Pitcairn Islands); and St Kilda (Scotland – a 'mixed' site also of cultural importance).

30 Margaret Thatcher withdrew the UK from UNESCO in 1985, Tony Blair rejoined in 1997, and Theresa May's government threatened to leave once more in 2018.

31 Including the 1954 International Convention for the Prevention of Pollution of the Sea by Oil; the 1972 London Convention (Convention on the Prevention of Marine Pollution by Dumping of Wastes and Other Matter); and the 1973 MARPOL (International Convention for the Prevention of Pollution from Ships).

Table 2. Principal international instruments relevant to UK biodiversity and the environment.

This is just a (very!) short selection of the main relevant instruments; there are many more,[32] including, notably, Agreements and Memoranda of Understanding (MoU) under CMS; protocols under CBD; marine and fisheries management organisations; and much other EU environmental legislation that the UK has implemented.

Date concluded	Title	Geographic scope
1931	Convention for the Regulation of Whaling	Global
1937	International Agreement for the Regulation of Whaling	Global
1946	International Convention for the Regulation of Whaling (ICRW)	Global
1971	Convention on Wetlands (Ramsar Convention)	Global
1972	World Heritage Convention	Global
1972	Convention for the Conservation of Antarctic Seals	Global
1975	Convention on International Trade in Endangered Species of Wild Fauna and Flora (CITES)	Global
1979	Convention on the Conservation of European Wildlife and Natural Habitats (Bern Convention)	Europe (and Africa)
1979	EU Directive on the conservation of wild birds (Birds Directive)	EU
1979	Convention on Migratory Species (CMS or Bonn Convention)	Global
1980	Convention for the Conservation of Antarctic Marine Living Resources	Global
1987	Montreal Protocol on Substances that Deplete the Ozone Layer	Global
1992	EU Directive on the conservation of natural habitats and of wild fauna and flora (Habitats Directive)	EU
1992	Convention on Biological Diversity (CBD)	Global
1992	Convention for the Protection of the Marine Environment of the North-East Atlantic (OSPAR Convention)[33]	NE Atlantic coastal states
1992	UN Framework Convention on Climate Change (UNFCCC)	Global
1994	Agreement on the Conservation of Small Cetaceans of the Baltic, North East Atlantic, Irish and North Seas (ASCOBANS)	Regional
1995	Agreement on the conservation of African-Eurasian migratory waterbirds (AEWA)	Regional
2000	EU Water Framework Directive	EU
2001	Agreement on the Conservation of Albatrosses and Petrels (ACAP)	Global
2008	EU Marine Strategy Framework Directive (MSFD)	EU
2015	EU Regulation on Invasive Alien Species	EU

32 For example, for the North Sea environment alone, and only to 1989, Freestone & Ijlstra (1990) list 45 relevant EU Directives, Decisions and Regulations; 88 Agreements, Conventions and treaties; and 21 primary and secondary national statutes. There have been many more in the subsequent 30 years!

33 OSPAR derived from two earlier Conventions (the 1971 Oslo Convention on the Prevention of Marine Pollution by Dumping from Ships and Aircraft, and the 1974 Paris Convention for the Prevention of Marine Pollution from Land-based Sources) related to different aspects of pollution control and reduction.

The highly conspicuous consequences of marine pollution from the 1960s created political pressure to resolve the problem. These oiled common guillemots (*Uria aalge*) were collected on the Dutch shoreline within one week in 1978. Although virtually all birds were contaminated with oil, most were only partly so. There was no particular oil spill known to have occurred immediately prior to this, indicating the extent of chronic, background marine pollution at that time.

for international treaties on migratory species and on trade in endangered species, as well as a commercial whaling moratorium. It also gave a fresh international outlook to environmental problems and their solutions, and started to linkeconomic development issues to the environment. The recommendations from that meeting are still very relevant and, while the conference had considerable influence in driving new processes, it also produced recommendations on problematic issues that remain topical today (Box C).

Despite an increasing need for treaties, Table 2 shows also that their development has reduced substantially since the turn of the millennium. While it can be contended that the important issues may, to a large extent, be covered by the existing suite of treaties, there appears to be a diminished contemporary political appetite for treaty-building.

Yet, even as early as 1980, the Brandt 'North-South' Commission on International Development Issues was highlighting problems that still have not gone away:

> '*such* [international] *deliberations have often ended in resolutions which exhort everyone, without binding or committing any of the parties; the differences are drafted away to create an appearance of agreement, but they persist in reality. One result of this process is that the language of international resolutions has become inbred, specialised and coded.*' (Brandt 1980)

The 'inbred' and 'coded' language has regrettably got worse rather than better in the four decades since. Formal linguistics analysis concluded that the IPCC 'summaries for policymakers – the bits that are supposed to be the most readable – are more complex than scientific papers by Albert Einstein or Stephen Hawking' (Black 2016).

Further, debate is often used tactically in order to avoid committing to actions (despite lip service to the Precautionary Principle,[34] which is explicitly written into some treaties such as CBD and AEWA and underlies all EU environmental legislation). The fisheries biologist John Gulland once memorably said: 'Fisheries management is interminable debate about the condition of fish stocks until all doubt is removed. And so are all the fish.'[35]

A total of 114 governments were represented at the 1972 UN Conference on the Human Environment in Stockholm. They reached an unprecedented level of agreement including, remarkably, a Declaration of Principles (Box C), and established institutional arrangements for international cooperation in environmental protection through the creation of the UNEP.

---

34 The Precautionary Principle recognises that delaying conservation action until there is robust evidence that it is needed to prevent significant harm will often result in such harm being more difficult/impossible to avert at a later stage (IUCN 2007). The Principle has been defined in a variety of ways, which vary in strength. Some provide simply that, 'Where there is a threat of significant reduction or loss of biological diversity, lack of full scientific certainty should not be used as a reason for postponing measures to avoid or minimize such a threat' (CBD Preamble); others explicitly call for precautionary measures, or even place an onus of proof on those proposing to undertake a potentially damaging activity to demonstrate that it will not result in environmental harm (see Cooney 2004).

In many contemporary conservation treaties, the Principle is interpreted as requiring Parties, in the case of uncertainty, to 'act in the best interest of the conservation of the species concerned' and 'adopt measures that are proportionate to the anticipated risks to the species' (e.g. some CITES and CMS resolutions). A common example of this approach is giving a species the benefit of the doubt in instances in which there is uncertainty as to whether it satisfies the criteria for listing in a particular category of protection. Typically, however, application requires explicit consideration of 'risk appetite' to determine the degree of precaution desirable in a defined situation. As outlined for whaling by Heazle (2006; Appendix 2), such practical application has proved extremely taxing (see also footnote 107).

35 Quoted by Sissenwine & Rosenberg (1993). See also Finlay (2011).

5 International treaties: how they work

Who can join?

Most of the major biodiversity conventions lie within the UN system, which restricts membership to its Member States. This excludes the formal UN Observer States of Palestine and Holy See, as well as other geopolitical entities such as Kosovo, Taiwan and Western Sahara. Some other international frameworks (for example the East Asian–Australasian Flyway Partnership) have wider membership that can include international organisations and NGOs.

Membership and growth

Following finalisation of negotiations, the text of an international instrument or treaty is signed by the national representatives present at that final meeting. This indicates the intent of a nation to join the instrument in due course. Others can join later by 'acceding' to the treaty. In most instances, however, signature alone is not sufficient to bind a state to a treaty (rather, it is simply a means of authenticating the treaty text),[36] and a subsequent ratification step is necessary, which, depending on national processes, may involve parliamentary approval.[37]

---

36 The term 'Signatory' is often used in a looser way, not just referring to those who signed the original act of adoption but also those who acceded later, since accession in practice also involves a signature of some kind.

37 However, a state that has signed a treaty but not yet expressed its consent to be bound is nevertheless obliged to refrain from acts that would defeat the treaty's purpose until such time as it has made clear that it does not intend to become a Party to the treaty – Vienna Convention on the Law of Treaties, Article 18. The upshot of this complexity is that some international instruments may have a few more Signatories than Parties.

Once an international instrument has been finalised through intergovernmental negotiations, it usually needs a minimum number of countries to ratify it for its provisions to enter into force. This can be a simple numerical threshold, but sometimes the situation is more complex. Thus, AEWA specified that it needed at least seven each of African and Eurasian Parties to ratify the Agreement before it came into legal effect. This was to ensure that early decisions were not dominated by Parties from only one region.

In the first few years after a Convention is agreed, a major task for Secretariat bodies (see below) and initial Contracting Parties is to promote membership to other potential Parties.

Why do countries become Parties to a Convention?

The answer to 'what's in it for them?' obviously depends on the nature of the specific treaty, but, as explored above, it often relates to joining a mechanism that will support or better facilitate national objectives. Thus, a migratory bird treaty provides support for national conservation through joint implementation of measures by all countries on a migratory route, while fisheries agreements, in theory, allow for catches and stock management to be undertaken on a shared, more sustainable, basis (but see Appendix 2 and Finlay 2011). Diplomatic peer pressure to promote accession by other countries is also important. A good example was the role of the Netherlands in the development of AEWA, first in sponsoring the Agreement and then diplomatically promoting accession by others once it was finalised (Boere 2010). National and international NGOs can also play an effective role in promoting the value of accession to potential new Parties.

Clearly, the more Parties that a Convention has, the more effective it can be (see Appendix 2 for the case of the IWC). Among the biodiversity-related conventions, CBD currently has most Parties (196), lacking only the USA from among UN Member States.[38] The history of the regulation of whaling, in which the UK has had a key role (both positive and negative at various times), offers a good example of the progressive evolution of international processes to address an objective (see Appendix 2).

Decision-making

The provisions of Conventions are binding on their Parties, although the strength of individual provisions depends on the language used. Hence, obligations (or subsequent decisions by COPs) using words such as 'shall', 'will' or 'must' imply a legally binding obligation. More typical – especially

---

38 The USA withdrew from other international processes under the presidency of Donald Trump, although under the Biden presidency it seems set to re-establish its more traditional, internationalist world view.

within Resolutions – is so-called softer language, with use of words such as 'encourage', 'seek to' or 'urge'.[39] This, and/or qualified language such as 'shall, as far as possible and as appropriate' and 'shall, subject to the availability of resources', gives Parties a significant degree of discretion as to whether, or how diligently, they will implement the action in question.

All MEAs involve a process of formal decision-making by a governing body which brings together Parties/Signatories. Typically, this is a COP or MOP – there is little technical difference. Decisions are variously called just that, or Resolutions, or sometimes Recommendations, for instance when addressing actors other than the Parties themselves.

Most MEAs take decisions by consensus – that is, collective agreement (or at least a recorded lack of active dissent) by all Parties present at the decision-making meeting. The consequence of this approach is that individual Parties can often exert considerable influence on the final decision through seeking removal of elements objectionable to their national interests, with the aim of achieving the all-important consensus. This does, however, risk that the final decision will reflect only a lowest common denominator agreeable to all. It is an approach that can lower targets and dilute the measures that are really needed to tackle the issues at stake. The ability to lodge

COPs of larger Conventions have been attended by thousands of delegates, as here at CITES COP 17 in 2016. The UK's hosting of UNFCCC COP 26 in 2020 was expecting 30,000 delegates and observers but was postponed due to the COVID-19 pandemic.

---

39 It is extraordinary that the choice between these seemingly innocuous (and already weak) alternatives is sometimes heatedly argued in negotiations!

Most MEA negotiations are undertaken in small 'contact groups' whose meetings often run through the night, as here at MOP 31 of the Montreal Protocol in 2019. The last session of that MOP formally closed at 00.33am after its final day extended through the subsequent night. Some meetings working to deadlines formally 'stop the clock' to create more time for final negotiations.

Delegates huddled to work on consensus text on climate change and wetlands at Ramsar COP 11, in 2012.

individual formal reservations or statements in the record of the meeting sometimes offers a useful way of addressing dissenting views and avoids blocking the consensus of all other Parties.[40]

The skill of negotiators is to craft language for decisions that facilitates agreement by all. This is often achieved through use of deliberate ambiguity or conditionality,[41] which allows for national interpretations of a decision.

---

40 The ICRW (Appendix 2) has an 'opt out' provision, allowing dissenting countries to legally reject a decision up to 90 days after it was taken. Such a mechanism is unusual, and typically in other forums dissenting Parties will either block consensus – resulting in no decision – or, in less significant cases, formally record that they do not consider themselves bound by the decision.

41 i.e. 'If this occurs, then that will happen…'

Unusually, although not uniquely, CITES COPs take decisions on species listings through a voting procedure, as here at COP 16 in 2013.

This is typically how MEAs move slowly forward (or at least manage to keep talking).

An example from the IWC records: 'Frequently when discussion on a particular topic was reaching a stalemate, the temporary solution was to put off consideration of any decision until the following year. Yet little change or progress was made at the next meeting, and as a result the situation remained deadlocked year after year, thus keeping the old [ineffective whaling] regulations comfortably in place' (Ivashchenko & Clapham 2014). Such scenarios are familiar from climate negotiations too.

With the great diversity of national, cultural, political and legal systems that exists it is unrealistic to expect that Conventions will easily set the leading edge by pioneering new standards and ideas. Part of their inherent purpose *is* to find the common denominator, and not necessarily to embody the very best practice (desirable though that would be). The important point is that, having found the common denominator, it is then enshrined in a legally robust and fixed way, and derives strength from the fact that it is (in principle) universally applicable. The task is then progressively to ratchet those standards forward – to raise the minimum regulatory 'floor' – in steps that cannot ever slide back, in effect moving the Overton window in relation to the issue.[42] There are many examples of this in practice, for example the progressive growth of multiple aspects of conservation in the marine environment.

In contrast to the consensus approach to decision-making, some MEAs, such as CITES (and the ICRW), regularly use a formal voting procedure to determine positions (also seen more recently in CMS),[43] especially when a decision *has* to be made – such as whether to list a species in an appendix.

---

42 The Overton window, developed in the mid-1990s by Joseph P. Overton, is the range of policies politically acceptable to the mainstream population at a given time. According to Overton, the window encompasses the policies that a politician can support without appearing too extreme to gain or keep public office, given the climate of public opinion at any time.

43 It is of interest that there have recently been more votes (or near votes) by Ramsar and CMS COPs – reflecting a trend towards increasingly legalistic approaches to negotiations. It took 40 years for Ramsar to take its first vote in 2011 – which concerned a decision about whether to have a vote on a substantive issue. Until that point, any contentious issues were always resolved through negotiation.

Secretariats and budgets

Most Conventions have a Secretariat (as established in legal texts) to stimulate, encourage, support and coordinate work desired by Parties – in the EU's case this is a role that is undertaken by the European Commission. These functions range from providing technical advice on national implementation issues (for example, in a Ramsar context, ensuring that wetlands of international importance proposed for designation do qualify), to organising necessary meetings and other activity to progress work that will be supportive of COP decisions. They ultimately report on their activities to all Parties at COP sessions, and intersessionally to a Standing Committee or equivalent governance structure appointed by the COP to act on its behalf.

Secretariats are normally funded through a budget paid by Parties and established by the COP for the subsequent planning period (Figure 1). The COP determines the size of the overall budget, while the size of each national 'slice' thereof is predetermined according to the size of national economies, typically following a UN-established scale.

Budgets determine the staffing levels of Secretariats and the scope of their activity. Since at least the early 2000s, Parties have typically failed to increase many MEA budgets, often resulting in real-terms reductions following inflation. This has had debilitating effects on the work of many treaties – not least since budgets have not always grown proportionately with increasing

Figure 1. Annual budgets for 2020 for principal biodiversity MEAs, with a selection of other environmental MEAs[44] (for abbreviations, see pp. 84–85). Note in particular: the relatively small budgets for subject and regionally limited CMS Agreements (green); the similarity of budgets for the IPBES and IPCC assessment processes (dark brown); and the large size of UNFCCC budget compared to global biodiversity conventions (Ramsar, CMS and even CBD).

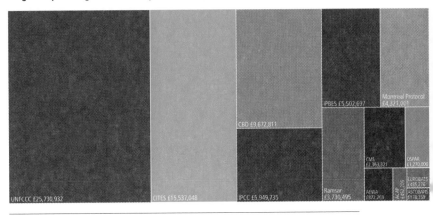

44   All converted to UK£ as at 1 April 2019. Figures are most recent budget Resolutions from each of the MEAs – with the exception of OSPAR, all are available on their respective websites.

numbers of Parties[45] and growing Party expectations.[46] Hence, many Secretariats now need to support more Parties and their requests, with the same or sometimes fewer resources. Furthermore, Parties are increasingly being called on to fund priority activities from voluntary contributions, which by their nature are not predictable and may be directed towards particular donor Party interests, rather than the Convention's highest priorities.

Secretariats are essentially small organisations and, as in any institution, their effectiveness varies according to the competence and leadership skills of their senior leader – typically called a Chief Executive Officer, Executive Secretary or Secretary General.

The sums that Parties collectively contribute to deal with the biodiversity crisis at international scales are trivial given the immensity of the issues that need to be addressed. The scale of investment and political interest in funding is related to the visibility, proximity and directness of the problem being considered. Typically, nature conservation loses because of the complex, indirect, often less visible, frequently indeterminate and long-term chain of causation between action and consequence – irrespective of the magnitude of that consequence. It is of interest that the scope of response that some have argued is necessary to address the climate and ecological crises has long been written off by decision-makers as unachievable fantasy (e.g. the need for universal consensus about seriousness; massive shifts in government funding; recalibration of economic expectations; framing with wartime language; suspension of certain civil liberties for the greater good) – and yet such radical changes have actually occurred in national responses to the COVID-19 pandemic.

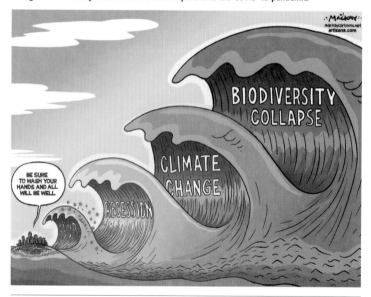

---

45 While each joining Party pays a contribution, these are not equal. For many MEAs, the more recent, and welcome, accessions of low-income countries therefore do not result in a pro-rata increase in budgetary contributions.

46 For instance, CMS has developed a range of comprehensive long-term, often global, Programmes of Work, including for flyways, marine mammals, and sharks, without the resources to implement even a few of the high-priority activities or resource the technical advisory bodies to support these. Thus typically, many remain 'paper programmes'.

A rich diversity of NGOs attend COPs, as here at CMS COP 11, 2015.

The role of NGOs

Although governments often give them little credit, national and international NGOs – together with the academic community – are hugely important in determining the effectiveness of MEAs. Their input can be structural: Ramsar (unusually) gives formal status to six international NGOs as 'International Organization Partners'.[47] Usually, however, NGOs contribute their expertise via scientific and governance subsidiary bodies, and within those bodies they have an important role in undertaking preparatory work on the texts that eventually come to be considered by COPs. They are also closely involved in the development of a range of technical documents, demonstration projects and international decision-support tools.[48] At formal meetings (Figure 2), NGOs have a further important role in helping to inform Parties of issues through side events, briefing and lobbying, as well as being the voice of concern for civil societies.

After the COP, NGOs can (if good relations exist) play an important national role in supporting a Party to implement the decisions made

Figure 2. The size of delegations to COPs is highly variable, as shown by formal registration for CITES COP 18 in 2019. Of 171 Parties attending, over half had delegations of fewer than three, although the USA attended with 43 and the UK with 26. The size of many of the 158 NGO delegations was more than most Party delegations (38 NGOs had more than three delegates).
■ = NGO delegations; ■ = Contracting Party delegations.

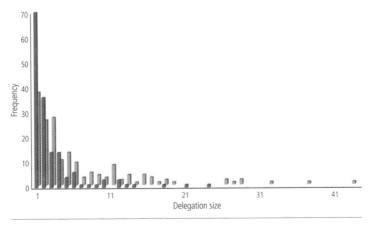

47 IUCN, World Wide Fund for Nature (WWF), BirdLife International, Wildfowl & Wetlands Trust (WWT), International Water Management Institute and Wetlands International.

48 For example, the Critical Site Network Tool for African–Eurasian migratory waterbird flyways.

There are many means of raising the profile of issues with national delegates! CMS COP 12, Manila, 2017.

(see below) as well as assisting those that require help, and by working with a range of Parties to foster international cooperation and action.

Scientific specialist groups are also crucial: inputting, for example, to IPCC special reports; to the 'GEO' reports; to the Millennium Ecosystem Assessment (2005) and drafting the various 'State of the World' reports (Table 1) such as those from the FAO Commission on Genetic Resources for Food and Agriculture. Yet NGOs often struggle to achieve the status and leverage that their expertise and 'on the ground' connectedness should really afford. Governments in general could do more to foster a genuine, ongoing and lasting partnership approach that better capitalises on the help that is available to them in this way. This would create a long-term 'win-win-win' for cooperation by ensuring that the trust needed to work together, which takes time to build and strengthen, is retained beyond the terms of particular individuals, governments and Secretariat staff.

Compliance

Holding Parties to account to deliver their agreed obligations can be critical for nature conservation. While Conventions are binding international law (at least in regard to the result to be achieved, if not the means to achieve it), there are rarely strong (or indeed any) compliance mechanisms to ensure that Parties honour the obligations they have agreed and hold them to account if they do not. For the UK, the EU was (prior to Brexit) unique in providing a strong compliance mechanism through the Commission and the European Court of Justice (ECJ) (Box D).

Some environmental treaties do provide for more stringent punitive measures, such as the use of trade sanctions in the Montreal Protocol and CITES (Sand 2013). These are, however, uncommon among the biodiversity-related treaties and, where available, tend to be considered measures of last resort, with the emphasis being on supporting compliance, more by opprobrium and peer pressure than enforcement.

Box D. EU compliance processes

The EU regards compliance with its environmental legislation as an important part of the 'level playing field' that achieves a single economic market. Historically, it has therefore developed explicit procedures to this end.

Compliance as established by EU treaties comprises several stages, of increasing formality. Initially, if the European Commission – the body charged with ensuring compliance – believes that a Member State is not adequately implementing Directive obligations, this is raised in the context of regular liaison meetings with the Member State. If there is no, or inadequate, progress, the Commission issues a formal warning letter to the Member State with a defined time to implement remedial measures and respond. If the situation persists after this, the case may be referred to the ECJ. And if the Member State ignores a subsequent ECJ ruling, under the Maastricht Treaty the Court can impose daily punitive fines until the situation is resolved.

A significant case for bird conservation, which had implications for the UK also, was case C-418/04 against Ireland in 2007. This related to a number of issues concerning inadequate implementation of Special Protection Area (SPA) provisions under the Birds Directive. The ECJ found comprehensively against Ireland, thereby triggering activity to identify and classify further SPAs in Ireland (and the UK).

One of the issues that the ECJ clarified was the legal requirement for a Member State to have at least some SPA provision for *all* species listed under Annex I of the Directive. At the time of the ruling, the UK had no classified SPAs for several regularly occurring Annex I species, including spoonbill (*Platalea leucorodia*), common crane (*Grus grus*), smew (*Mergus albellus*), white-tailed eagle (*Haliaeetus albicilla*), Montagu's harrier (*Circus pygargus*) and kingfisher (*Alcedo atthis*). The third review of the UK SPA network (Stroud *et al.* 2016) has since identified sites for these species (although as of April 2021 no classification of them has yet occurred).

It is possible for a third party to challenge a Member State in national courts on national non-compliance. In the UK, such a case, brought to the High Court in 1999 by Greenpeace, led to the application of the Nature Directives in all UK waters (to 200 nautical miles), not just territorial waters (to 12 nautical miles).

Unfortunately, lack of enforcement mechanisms, along with the soft, caveated, language of many treaties and decisions, gives Parties enormous latitude for non-compliance. Typically, the main means of highlighting such lack of implementation is the public 'naming and shaming' of recalcitrant Parties. This usually relies on NGOs, because for diplomatic reasons Parties are generally reluctant to complain about non-implementation by other States. Nonetheless, there are examples of even relatively weak compliance mechanisms being effective in altering state behaviour (Box E).

Another, not unusual, outcome occurs when avenues for redress do not give a positive conservation outcome in the case concerned, but subsequently provide an arena in which implementation challenges can be examined, loopholes exposed, and interpretations tested and firmed up. This can be thought of as losing the battle but gaining in the war. A good UK example of this is the land claim of internationally important estuarine mudflats within a Site of Special Scientific Interest (SSSI) at Lappel Bank on the Medway, in Kent, in the early 1990s (Pritchard 1997; Williams *et al.* 2005). Although the area was ultimately destroyed and is now a car park, it led to a 1996 ECJ ruling (C-44/95) related to principles of boundary setting for EU Natura 2000 sites that has since been of critical importance across Europe. This has provided fundamental jurisprudence that has shaped the European Natura 2000 network on the basis of scientific objectivity rather than sites that are politically convenient through their lack of economic importance.

In some countries, however, the lack of legal standing for NGOs can severely inhibit their ability to challenge the state. For example, in Poland 'in practice NGOs do not enjoy legal standing to challenge local laws that contravene national law relating to environment, unless these NGOs are injured in their own right' (European Commission 2019a). This is a particularly important constraint in non-democracies beyond the EU.

On very rare occasions, a state's non-compliance in relation to biodiversity can come before the International Court of Justice (ICJ). However, using this approach can be problematic – as was demonstrated by Japan's response to the ICJ's unfavourable judgment regarding its whaling (Clapham 2015; Appendix 2). Following the ruling, Japan filed an amended declaration regarding national acceptance of the ICJ jurisdiction, but in which it excluded 'any dispute arising out of, concerning, or relating to research on,

NGOs can have a significant role in focusing pubic attention, via media interest, on environmental problems. Protests by Friends of the Earth Scotland against peat-cutting at Duich Moss, on Islay (see Box E), significantly raised the profile of this case with the UK government and the European Commission, resulting in its successful resolution.

or conservation, management or exploitation of, living resources of the sea'. In this way, Japan has simply removed the ICJ's future remit in respect of any further potential cases related to living resources in the marine environment.

The European Union and its Nature Directives

EU governance structures have had major consequences for the UK's environment. Most recent international Conventions allow for Regional Economic Integration Organisations (such as the EU and the African Union) to become Parties in the same way as individual countries. When this occurs, the EU has 'competency' in coordinating a joint EU position with the Member

Box E. The value of compliance

Eilean na Muice Duibhe (Duich Moss) Ramsar Site and SPA in Scotland is the most important roost site for Greenland white-fronted geese in the UK.

The Greenland white-fronted goose (*Anser albifrons flavirostris*), of which the UK holds about half the world population every winter, has twice benefited from actions taken to hold the UK to its obligations. In 1985, when planning permission was given for commercial peat-cutting on Eilean na Muice Duibhe (Duich Moss) on Islay, in Scotland, the European Commission initiated proceedings against the UK for breach of Article 4 of the Birds Directive. Following that intervention, peat was taken from elsewhere on Islay and Duich Moss is now protected as an SPA and Ramsar Site (Stroud 1985; Greenland White-fronted Goose Study 1986). More recently, the Welsh government repeatedly refused to give statutory protection to the geese from shooting in Wales, despite an explicit legal obligation on the UK to do so under AEWA. Intervention by AEWA's formal compliance mechanism, the Implementation Review Process, in 2018 has now resulted in the species being protected from shooting in both Wales and England from September 2020 (Greenland White-fronted Goose Study in draft; HMSO 2020a,b).

States.[49] On some issues such as fisheries – an internationally shared resource – the European Commission has exclusive competency to develop a position on behalf of the EU. According to the subject area, sometimes the EU position is presented at a COP by the Commission, or sometimes by the particular Member State which holds the rotating Presidency of the Union at that time.

Whatever the legal details, such a common position from a block of 27 Parties (formerly 28, before the UK's withdrawal in 2020) is very powerful in international negotiations – albeit that discussions within the EU to achieve that shared view may be lengthy and difficult (and may indeed result in no decision or clear line to take, leading to formal abstention in voting, or a weak, lowest common denominator position).

The UK's departure from the EU poses serious risks to standards of environmental protection, especially the removal of strong compliance mechanisms (Box D) that hold government to the environmental obligations it has assumed, and for which proposed domestic replacements look far from sufficient and have yet to be introduced. That said, some aspects of EU policy, most notably the Common Agricultural Policy, have driven significant harm to nature and to natural systems, and here the promise (as yet unrealised) of a new domestic approach which confines the payment of public money to the delivery of public goods, could mark a significant improvement in the state of nature in the farmed environment.

There is also a risk that there may be an appetite to replace well-established processes and priorities, developed in partnership with EU States, with unique UK approaches, without reference to their efficacy. While there is always room for improvement, including of existing EU processes, it is important that any such improvements build on existing systems and lessons learnt, and avoid causing delays and disruption that would take time we do not have, given the urgency of the challenges we face.

Many aspects of environmental protection are inherently international in nature, with neither species, habitats nor many of the factors that drive their decline respecting national boundaries. As such, there is a clear and ongoing imperative for international cooperation and alignment. The UK, outside the EU, could take this opportunity to be ambitious, but risks having less influence on environmental policy development, and becoming increasingly remote from wider thinking and ideas within the EU and beyond, unless the UK government take proactive steps to rebuild lines of communication and forums for engagement.

Much EU legislation and policy responds to the need to implement, at EU scale, wider international obligations. Thus, the two Nature Directives are

---

49 In other words: legal authority. EU Treaties specify that for some issues the European Commission has 'competence' to determine policy rather than the Member States – a good example being fisheries.

EU common positions are agreed ahead of international meetings, but delegations of EU Parties meet at least daily during a COP to track negotiations and, as necessary, revise positions, as here at CMS COP 12 in 2017.

EU positions on issues arising often need to be agreed 'in real time' during final debates, as here at CBD's Ad Hoc Open-ended Working Group on Protected Areas, 2005.

the mechanism by which obligations under the Council of Europe's Bern Convention on the Conservation of European Wildlife and Natural Habitats are implemented within EU legislation.[50] Accordingly, there is great similarity between obligations under Bern and those of the EU Birds and Habitats Directives. This has major implications now that the UK has left the EU, since essentially the same international obligations (for example, on species and habitat protection) persist, albeit deriving from a different legal instrument. There will, however, probably be a lower standard for ensuring compliance internationally, since mechanisms under Bern do not involve legal process in the way that the ECJ does.[51]

---

50 Similarly, Britain's 1981 Wildlife and Countryside Act (W&CA) arose from the same imperatives: the UK could not ratify the Bern Convention until domestic enabling legislation had been enacted.

51 Compliance mechanisms under Bern involve essentially an administrative assessment of issues by the annual meeting of its Standing Committee, rather than any legal process as with the ECJ.

Table 3. **National and global assessments of the Aichi Targets for biodiversity 2011–2020.**

For UK government assessment (JNCC 2019b): orange = progress towards target but at an insufficient rate; grey = insufficient data to draw a conclusion; green = on track to achieve target; white = no assessment made. For Royal Society for the Protection of Birds (RSPB) assessment of UK performance (RSPB 2020): red = no progress or moving away from the target (a = moving away from target; b = 'a serious case to be made for "moving away from target"'); orange = progress towards the target at an insufficient rate; grey = insufficient data to draw a conclusion; green = meeting or exceeding target; white = not assessed. For CBD global assessment (CBD 2020b): red = target not achieved; orange = target partially achieved.

Aichi Targets	UK government assessment	RSPB assessment of UK performance	CBD global assessment
1. Communication and public awareness			
2. Biodiversity values into national accounting and plans			
3. Eliminate harmful subsidies			
4. Sustainable production and consumption			
5. Halve rate of habitat loss and degradation			
6. Sustainable fish stocks			
7. Sustainable agriculture, aquaculture & forestry			
8. Tackle pollution			
9. Invasive alien species			
10. Climate: conserve coral reefs			
11. Effective protected areas: >17% land and >10% sea		a	
12. Prevent extinction & improve species status		b	
13. Maintain genetic diversity			
14. Safeguard ecosystem services			
15. Carbon stocks, restore >15% degraded ecosystems			
16. Benefit sharing: Nagoya Protocol			
17. National biodiversity strategies			
18. Indigenous peoples & local communities			
19. Enhance and share knowledge & technology			
20. Mobilize financial resources		b	

There is also close interaction between the EU and other international processes. Thus, obligations under CBD have been influential in framing the EU's Biodiversity Strategy (European Commission 2011, 2020), which in turn guides the development of relevant European policy.

Where different international instruments address the same issue, negotiations can become complex because decisions taken in relation to one international framework have implications not only nationally but also for the other framework(s) (Epstein 2013).[52] An example is the complexity of recent discussions on European goose management being taken forward under AEWA, which also has implications for application of the EU Birds Directive in the same countries. Accordingly, and due to the political difficulties in amending EU legislation, certain more recent non-EU treaties are modelled on EU legislation rather than the other way around.[53]

The role of the Convention on Biological Diversity

The CBD is pre-eminent among biodiversity-related MEAs, both in terms of its resources (its 2020 operational budget is US$12,562,000 – CBD 2019, Figure 1) and its political importance: CBD COPs routinely secure a 'high-level' ministerial part of the Conference, which is an opportunity for networking of, and advocacy with, national environment ministers.

The two global Strategic Plans for Biodiversity negotiated through CBD are of particular note, as these have set international agendas for reduction of biodiversity loss. In April 2002, the Parties committed themselves to achieve by 2010 'a significant reduction of the current rate of biodiversity loss at the global, regional and national level as a contribution to poverty alleviation and to the benefit of all life on Earth'. The 2010 target was subsequently endorsed by the World Summit on Sustainable Development and UN General Assembly, and was incorporated as a new target under the MDGs. However, with the failure to achieve this target (CBD 2010b), the next Strategic Plan established 20 more detailed targets (often called the 'Aichi Biodiversity Targets', named after the prefecture in Japan where they were negotiated), essentially to achieve much the same aims by 2020 (although this time better reflecting human development needs). No targets were achieved in full, and only six were partly achieved (CBD 2020b; Table 3).

The CBD's COP 15 (originally scheduled for 2020 but postponed to late 2021) will debate a new 'Post-2020 Global Biodiversity Framework' which is currently subject to considerable international discussion. This will establish a critical agenda for national and international actions for the next decade and beyond (most likely with a '2030 Mission' and a '2050 Vision' – CBD 2020a). Given the worldwide biodiversity crisis, there is an urgency, driven

---

52 Such overlaps can be used to delay having to take decisions on issues that Parties would prefer to avoid. An example related to the mandate to regulate hydrofluorocarbons which was passed back and forth for years between the Montreal Protocol and the UNFCCC, until finally the Kigali Amendment to the Montreal Protocol was adopted in 2016.

53 Thus, AEWA's provisions largely mirror those of the EU Birds Directive. Yet while it can be argued that this extends European good practice here, there is a degree of unreality as to the practicalities of applying many of the detailed regulatory provisions in developing countries.

by considerable public and civil society momentum, to raise the political will to be much more ambitious in setting high targets – since these targets will provide obligations against which NGOs can then exert pressure for action (Table 3).

An expression of the failure to meet these global targets is the unprecedented and ongoing loss of global biodiversity (IPBES 2019), as well as continuing climate change. Much rides on whether governments can show robust leadership by avoiding sinking to the lowest common denominator approach of the past, and instead generating a political paradigm shift. And to that end, public and high-level[54] calls for a post-pandemic 'new normal' create helpful political space for governments to be more ambitious.

---

54 For example by UN Secretary-General António Guterres in January 2021: www.un.org/sg/en/content/sg/speeches/2021-01-11/remarks-one-planet-summit

6 How do treaties work on a national level?

Transposition into UK law

When a country formally becomes a Party to an international instrument, in most cases the requirements of that instrument need to be legally transposed into domestic law. Sometimes, where the treaty involves a new or emerging issue, this means new primary legislation (i.e. Acts of Parliament). A good UK example was the 2008 Climate Change Act, which established a range of new legal obligations for the UK government in response to the UNFCCC. More often, however, a simple updating or tweaking of existing legislation is all that is needed to enshrine the new commitments in law.

EU Directives typically establish a policy objective but are not prescriptive as to how Member States should achieve it.[55] Thus, when the 1992 Habitats Directive came into force it required no new primary legislation, since the UK's 1981 Wildlife and Countryside Act (W&CA) already provided a good national framework.[56] However, several secondary instruments (the Habitats Regulations) were needed to transpose some of the Directive's more detailed requirements into UK law.[57]

---

55 This at least was the original intention, although both the Nature Directives are mostly prescriptive (or have become so with case law). The Marine Strategy Framework Directive (MSFD) is more objective/target driven, but certain Member States wish to add legally binding prescriptions, which creates tension.

56 Sheail (1998) and Housden (2015) provide excellent accounts of the genesis of the W&CA. The Act was originally stimulated to implement the Birds Directive and the Bern Convention, both dating from 1979.

57 Statutory Instruments, which are not debated in the way that Acts of Parliament are.

Sometimes no new specific laws are required if existing provisions are deemed adequate. So, the requirements of CMS (which the UK joined in 1985) could also be fulfilled by the W&CA, while the range of obligations under Ramsar were considered to be covered by the W&CA and other UK environmental legislation (for example in relation to water quality and site protection).

After transposition of a treaty, subsequent decisions by the COP can also result in the need for new national legislation (for instance, implementation of climate-related commitments under the UNFCCC's Paris Agreement will require wide-ranging new legislation for ratifying States).[58] International decisions can also have significant impacts on government policy. Thus, England's '25 Year Environment Plan' (Defra 2018) was heavily influenced by the Aichi Biodiversity Targets (see Table 3 above), as were the equivalent strategies in Scotland (Scottish Government 2013),[59] Wales and Northern Ireland.

Nation-states have different approaches to interactions between international obligations and national legislation (Finlayson & Gardner 2018). Some will not sign a treaty unless they first have the national legislation to implement it, while others use signing as the spur to develop relevant national statutes. As an example, some countries (such as the UK) will not designate a Ramsar Site unless the site is *already* covered by relevant national protection mechanisms,[60] while others use that international designation as the first step *towards* eventual national protection.

Accession of Overseas Territories and Crown Dependencies

The UK's Overseas Territories and Crown Dependencies are entirely self-governing, in contrast to the political situation of territories of other countries such as France. Therefore, when the UK accedes to an MEA, each relevant entity needs separately to agree to accede to it and, upon doing so, to introduce relevant statutes as necessary and appropriate. Sometimes this agreement process is undertaken ahead of the UK signature, but historically, it has more often occurred afterwards.

Holding national governments to account

It is in the nature of national governments around the world to undertake to do something but then to just never quite get around to doing all that

---

58 An important exception relates to those treaties with dynamic lists of species to which different types of protection or policy apply (such as CITES and AEWA). International decisions to amend these lists need subsequent national transposition (unless reservations have been entered).

59 Scottish Parliament established a legal requirement to report on the delivery of the Scottish Biodiversity Strategy which was informed by both the Aichi Targets and the EU Biodiversity Strategy: www.gov.scot/publications/scottish-biodiversity-strategy-report-parliament-2017-2019/pages/3/. No such assessment and report-back process occurs in the other UK countries.

60 Such as prior legal notification as an SSSI in Britain or an Area of Special Scientific Interest in Northern Ireland.

Box F. Development of UK marine conservation frameworks and marine SPA problems

The development of marine conservation policy in the UK offers a good example of the cascade of actions that can arise from a new international instrument, and the problems of implementation.

In 2008, the EU adopted its Marine Strategy Framework Directive (MSFD), requiring Member States to achieve multiple marine conservation objectives. It was drafted (after some debate) as fundamentally goal-setting, rather than being prescriptive of legislative requirements.

To implement this, the UK passed both primary (Marine and Coastal Access Act 2009; Marine (Scotland) Act 2010; Marine Act (Northern Ireland) 2013) and much secondary legislation (including parts of the Offshore Marine Conservation (Natural Habitats, &c.) (Amendment) Regulations 2012). The legislation gave new regulatory powers to the Marine Management Organisation in England, and to Marine Scotland (although the latter is now just a department within Scottish Government and no longer provides any independent regulatory function).

The interactions between the 1992 Habitats Directive and later MSFD are complex. In particular, problems relate to transferring essentially terrestrial approaches to marine conservation (for example in relation to species and site protection, monitoring and reporting obligations).

Implementation of the Birds Directive in marine waters has been proceeding at near-glacial speed. Marine SPA provision has long been recognised as insufficient (Stroud *et al.* 1990; Williams *et al.* 2005), with a first review of potential such sites undertaken by the NCC in 1989 (but not published).

The failure by the UK government to progress the issue led in 2012 to a formal complaint by the Royal Society for the Protection of Birds (RSPB) to the European Commission, related to multiple issues of marine non-implementation of the Directive. In response, UK government committed to the Commission that year to a 'target of identifying marine SPAs by 2015 and classifying as many of these as possible by then' (JNCC 2013). This target has been repeatedly pushed into the future. While a designation programme has slowly begun elsewhere in UK waters, in Scotland there has been little progress. In 2014, Scottish Natural Heritage made proposals to Scottish Government for the creation of 14 marine SPAs and these were discussed at a stakeholder workshop in 2016. Three years later, the Joint Nature Conservation Committee (JNCC) (2019a) reported optimistically: 'Identification of fully marine SPA is now complete, and many sites are classified, with the remainder having been consulted upon. Decisions on designations will be made shortly.' Eventually, in late December 2020, nine new marine SPAs were classified in Scottish waters, with marine extensions to a further two Scottish firths. However, the supporting work undertaken by the JNCC to demonstrate the sufficiency of the UK marine network, and which commenced in 2015, has yet to be published as of March 2021.

has been committed to (for a wide variety of reasons). In the UK, action to implement government decisions can be conveniently avoided for years by establishing Working Groups or other consultative mechanisms – as was accurately satirised by the 1970s television series *Yes Minister*.

In democracies, a key role in ensuring implementation of international decisions, and holding governments to account through the formal compliance mechanisms described above, is played by the advocacy of NGOs on behalf of and in conjunction with civil society.[61] Indeed, there are multiple UK examples of well-organised campaigns changing government policy in the face of vested or political interests (Box G).[62] Although there are no useful or reliable international statistics, it is likely that the UK is particularly rich in the number, size, membership and influence of its environmental NGOs.

The routine cycle of large international meetings (a Convention typically convening its COP every three years or so) provides a particularly important opportunity for national NGOs to hold governments publicly to account if they are failing to fulfil their obligations. There is always a flurry of activity within governments ahead of COPs or MOPs to resolve particularly problematic issues so that national 'dirty linen' is not aired on an international stage.

Such pressure, however, is considerably less than it should be given the large body of unimplemented international commitments. There is a widespread view that the UK's 2014 Lobbying Act is restricting advocacy by the charity sector (Sheila McKechnie Foundation 2018). Few NGOs have the financial or human resources for major and prolonged advocacy efforts, meaning that the public remains ill-informed about many environmental issues, even in a country such as the UK where there has been so much action on several fronts.

Environmental monitoring and use of the resulting information to inform about the state of implementation of commitments is a very important element of national accountability. In recent years, publications such as *The State of Nature 2019* (Hayhow *et al.* 2019, and previous reports since 2013)[63] have been very influential in relating the condition of the UK's natural environment to international obligations.

A central obligation of nearly all MEAs is to require a periodic national report on progress. While the responsibility for that lies with government, in the UK consultative processes give an important opportunity for dialogue with NGOs. Indeed, NGOs play a huge role in the provision of relevant environmental data for UK reporting – especially for biodiversity. Although this effort may be supported by government funding, the threat that funding

---

61 However, it is important to note that the NGOs best at influencing MEAs and the Parties that attend their meetings are mostly drawn from the richer 'West'. Few NGOs represent civil society in Africa or other developing parts of the world. Some of the interest groups representing large conservation organisations, or business and industry, have delegations to COPs that significantly exceed those of the countries they are seeking to influence (see Figure 2).

62 Of course, NGO interests can also be considered vested and in many cases are markedly single-issue. Such lack of broader balance can lead to NGO campaigns that may be at odds with desirable conservation outcomes as determined from broader perspectives.

63 The first *State of Nature* report was initiated by a consortium of 25 NGOs, joined for later issues by the UK statutory agencies.

Box G. Holding governments to deliver their obligations

Good examples of successful public campaigns that changed government policy include:

- The Campaign for Lead-Free Air (CLEAR) successfully lobbied to remove toxic tetraethyl lead from petrol in the late 1970s and early 1980s (Rogers 1983; Wilson 1983, 1984; Stroud 2015);
- In the mid-1980s, pressure from NGOs marshalled by RSPB, and the government's NCC, ultimately achieved a major change of government policy with respect to the destructive afforestation of internationally important peatlands in the Flow Country of northern Scotland (Tompkins 1986; Bainbridge *et al.* 1987; Stroud *et al.* 1987, 2015) (see pp. 5–6). Since then, increased recognition of the extent to which unplanted peatlands can be degraded by the presence of adjacent plantations (Wilson *et al.* 2014) has led to a greater commitment to remove these forest blocks and restore blanket bog – initiated with EU LIFE funding;
- The multi-NGO Peatland Campaign initiated the move away from peat-based garden 'composts' in the late 1990s and pressured government to buy out commercial peat-cutting rights at several internationally important peatlands, including Thorne and Hatfield Moors (Stoneman 2016);
- For many years those highlighting the risks of marine plastic pollution were gaining little traction with government. However, public outrage following David Attenborough's BBC series *Blue Planet II* in 2017 acted as a trigger for a cascade of policy initiatives – highlighting the important role of the media;

Strandline plastic pollution in North Queensferry, Scotland.

- In 2016, environmental NGOs across the EU campaigned to defend the Nature Directives from the potential for renegotiation and the risk of diluting their provisions (a 'fitness check' process). This campaign employed robust science, such as analyses of the effect of Natura 2000 protected areas on continent-wide bird population trends, as well as powerful advocacy;[64]
- Recent campaigns have led to a commitment to the licensing of grouse moors and legal protection for mountain hares (*Lepus timidus*) in Scotland.

Over half a million submissions were made to the European Commission calling to protect the EU's Nature Directives, significantly more than for any other EU consultation in history.

64 www.wwf.eu/?287170/Nature-dodges-bullet-huge-public-campaign-saves-EU-nature-laws

may either be reduced or withdrawn hangs over many if not most programmes: hence the political importance of demonstrable public support. A pertinent example was the public petition to the Scottish Parliament highlighting strong support for better integrated structures for biological recording. This has subsequently developed as the innovative Scottish Biodiversity Information Forum,[65] which proposes ways to improve data flows and governance to assist with national reporting for Scotland.

65 nbn.org.uk/wp-content/uploads/2018/11/SBIF-Review-Final-Report-and-Recommendations.pdf

7 National implementation

The UK is a relatively small island group lying off a continental land-mass, yet many features of its environment are of international importance. Its oceanic (and in places hyper-oceanic) climate has created the greatest extent of blanket bog of any country (Lindsay *et al.* 1988), and these wet temperate conditions also support other internation-ally distinctive landscapes such as oceanic woodlands and bryophyte-rich habitats (Ratcliffe 1968). The seas around the UK support important and distinctive habitats, including cold-water coral reefs and maerl beds (sublittoral coralline red algae found widely off Atlantic shores), while UK seabird populations are of great international significance (Mitchell *et al.* 2004). The UK's location also means that it is of major importance also for boreal breeding waterbirds that migrate to spend the non-breeding season on its massive and food-rich estuaries, where large tidal ranges and a mild climate (thanks to the influence of the Gulf Stream) provide excellent foraging opportunities throughout the winter.

Overseas Territories

A colonial legacy, the 14 Overseas Territories form part of the UK, while the three Crown Dependencies (the separate Bailiwicks of Guernsey and Jersey, and the Isle of Man) are not part of the UK but are self-governing dependencies of the Crown. Together, these territories have enormous global

The UK has the world's greatest extent of blanket bog. Islay, Scotland.

biodiversity significance,[66] and include some of the biggest seabird colonies in the world (Gough and Inaccessible Islands, Tristan da Cunha);[67] extensive coral reef systems in the British Indian Ocean Territory and territories in the Caribbean; major populations of marine turtles; a diversity of endemic flora and fauna; and much else besides (Oldfield *et al.* 1999). In 2016, the UK government designated more than 800,000km² of waters around the Pitcairn Islands as a Marine Protected Area – one of the largest in the world (albeit one that lacks any enforcement). In 2019, the UK government announced a further massive protected area, of 687,000km², in the waters of Tristan da Cunha.[68] This will close over 90% of Tristan's waters to harmful activities such as bottom-trawling fishing, sand extraction and deep-sea mining.

Drawing attention to the conservation needs on these islands has been a difficult challenge, but there has been greater recognition in recent years thanks to the work of the UK Overseas Territories Conservation Forum, and profile-raising within the UK government by the JNCC.

The UK government published a biodiversity strategy for the UK Overseas Territories over a decade ago (Defra 2009). Without going into detail here, sustaining the focus that the strategy provided has been challenging, not least because of constantly changing Foreign Office, and Department for Environment, Food and Rural Affairs (Defra) ministers and officials,

---

66 Considerable information about the biodiversity of the Overseas Territories and Crown Dependencies can be found on the website of the UK Overseas Territories Conservation Forum (www.ukotcf.org.uk).

67 These islands are protected as both Ramsar and World Heritage Sites.

68 www.gov.uk/government/news/worlds-most-remote-island-helps-uk-exceed-protected-ocean-target

The Turks and Caicos Islands hold one major Ramsar Site, but many of their other internationally important wetlands are unprotected. The 'Hog River' in East Caicos is a brackish waterway fed by rain from nearby hills and supporting outstanding biodiversity. It is ecologically very fragile and at risk from development.

exacerbated by reorganised departmental structures and portfolios over time. To further complicate matters, there are major differences between the ways in which portfolios within Overseas Territory and Crown Dependency governments are arranged on the one hand, and the way these are allocated within UK government and the devolved administrations on the other. There may be differences, for example, in whether environment and farming (and climate change and energy) are considered in separate units or in a more integrated way.[69] This can make organising meetings of 'counterpart' officials and ministers problematic.

National decision-making

The role of ministers is crucial to the UK's implementation of international obligations and agreement to any new decisions. UK delegations to some recent COPs have gone with the negotiating instruction not to agree to any new commitments; in other words, with instructions to water down the text of decisions in order to turn them into non-binding, aspirational language only. At other times, such as under former Secretary of State for the Environment Michael Gove, the message to officials has been, in effect, 'go out and make a difference' (see also King 2020). This latter stance represents a refreshing

---

69 For example, in Bermuda the government has a single Ministry for Environment and Natural Resources, which includes both environment and agriculture, while in the Turks and Caicos Islands there are separate Ministries for Tourism, Environment, Heritage, Maritime and Gaming; and also for Health, Agriculture, Human Services and Sports. Responsibility for climate change issues is widely variable within Overseas Territory and Crown Dependency governments.

change which, unsurprisingly, resulted in positive outcomes – including direct engagement in governance processes of several MEAs for the first time in decades.

Critical also is the role of senior civil servants within Defra, and the extent to which they are prepared to seek strong negotiating mandates from ministers in advance of COPs or equivalent meetings, and – just as important – to seek to implement decisions through new policy and initiatives on their return. Individuals (see p. 71) can be key in moving government thinking and policy forward, but only if they are prepared to argue against the innate conservatism of the government machine and constantly to push for action against prevailing 'do nothing' tendencies.[70]

Both in its own right and during its time as part of the EU family, the UK has had a history of considerable influence in international meetings, especially within the EU. Not least, this is a result of the natural advantage that the UK has by virtue that English is a dominant language of many decision-text negotiations (see p. 6), and also because of a certain historical legacy of assumed leadership in some of the more arcane arts of political diplomacy.

Engagement with NGOs

In marked contrast to some other countries, the UK government is credited with a generally mature relationship with most environmental NGOs.[71] NGO representatives tend to have good access to officials and strong engagement on issues, for instance as part of the preparation of national positions in advance of Convention COPs. However, this is not universal: for example, the UK Natura 2000 and Ramsar Forum, which formally brought together government and NGOs on issues concerning the implementation of that Convention, has not been convened by government since 2010, which weakens opportunities to discuss these matters at a UK scale. And since the environment is a devolved responsibility, NGO engagement with the devolved administrations is just as important (and in most cases could be much improved by government, to the benefit of the administrations concerned).

The House of Commons Environment, Transport and Rural Affairs Select Committee noted in 1999 that 'NGOs perform a vital role during the negotiation of MEAs. We would like to see opportunities being made available

---

70 A problem of British governance that is scarcely new (Nicholson 1967).

71 The situation is especially problematic where the ability of an NGO to provide services (such as running monitoring schemes or other support) is economically dependent on a state. There are examples of States threatening to halt such funding following conservation advocacy challenges. This situation has occurred in the EU, especially in small and/or politically less mature countries. Sometimes situations arise where NGOs are blacklisted by their environment ministries even though they hold data and expertise highly relevant for national reporting to MEAs.

to them to extend that role and to have a greater influence on those who are negotiating the detailed provisions of agreements. Where appropriate, this could include more involvement in Government delegations, especially where this enhances the competence of the UK to negotiate' (House of Commons 1999). This has only rarely occurred.[72]

Existing coordination within government

Prior to a COP, the government develops an internal position on each of the proposed decisions. In reaching that position, the papers are circulated to other government departments that may have an interest, as well as the devolved governments (and, where relevant, Overseas Territory or Crown Dependency governments). Thus, the final position (in theory at least) represents a joined-up view across UK government. Typically, however, follow-up after the preparatory meetings is seldom regular and is markedly ad hoc. The extent to which NGOs can influence such positions, or implementation thereafter, generally varies considerably depending on openness to dialogue by the individual senior officials responsible. These problems are of long standing, having been identified in the House of Commons Environment, Transport and Rural Affairs review of UK engagement with MEAs in 1999, and had seemingly been the norm for some time before that.

While a certain amount of stakeholder engagement occurs before some MEA COPs, this is an inconsistent process, with no means by which the public may readily access information about UK aims for a particular meeting. More concerning still is the lack of information (either for the public or parliamentarians) following meetings as to new obligations agreed, their implications for the UK, or how government plans to deliver these.

How coordination could be improved

Periodic overviews of how coordination could be improved, or synergies exploited, are rare but have the potential to be highly valuable. The JNCC convened a workshop in 2009 to consider the UK process of engagement with MEAs and how it could be improved.[73] In particular, it reflected on the fact that a number of issues (for example climate, invasive alien species, emerging infectious diseases, illegal trade) were being addressed in separate international forums (CBD, CMS, Ramsar, AEWA etc.), yet there was no single and joined-up UK view on these matters – thus potentially missing synergies between them. Nor was there any systematic process of feeding back

---

72 The counterargument is that it is better to have close cooperation between government and national NGOs at a COP which recognises their different roles, yet does not bind NGO representatives to follow strict government lines, which would be the case if they were formally part of the national delegation.

73 webarchive.nationalarchives.gov.uk/20110704150839/http://jncc.defra.gov.uk/page-4663-theme=print

outcomes of key meetings to government and non-government stakeholders, including the public and parliamentarians.

The workshop concluded that there was a need to 'identify over the next few years, between Government, its agencies and NGOs, a strategic UK agenda and priorities in preparation for the next round of MEA meetings. This can be both in terms of disseminating what is happening, and the policy needs for science evidence/capacity development, and also in terms of informing the general public what is going on' (JNCC 2009). Regrettably, there has been no progress in this direction since then, and input to individual international processes remains largely undertaken within the context of each MEA, rather than as part of any larger government vision. Such a situation would be regrettable at the best of times, but it is even more problematic in the context of the austerity cuts that followed the recession of 2007–2009 and consequent loss of resources across the UK's four governments. Tackling difficult policy areas is made considerably more challenging by inefficient modes of working and weak stakeholder engagement.

The growing devolution of UK political structures has also brought challenges, especially in view of the fact that international negotiations are undertaken by Defra on behalf of the UK government, yet the responsibility for implementation of environmental issues is devolved to country governments[74] (although the UK government retains responsibility for offshore waters, beyond 12 nautical miles from the coast, in practice much is now devolved to the separate countries). Increasingly, the relevance of other policy sectors to biodiversity issues (and the benefits that achievement of biodiversity goals can offer them in return) also demands a more cross-cutting approach, which has been slow to develop in the UK. In common with countries that have full political federalism (e.g. France, Germany, Spain), it is sometimes difficult if not impossible to define a single UK position or policy. Resolution of this *might* be feasible *if* there were strong political leadership, resources to support demonstration of actions and, most importantly, a willingness by all to follow the defined international agenda. Realistically, this probably awaits a more stable constitutional settlement within the UK.

UK government priorities

Prior to the current period of formal government austerity, Defra was already developing revised priorities for engagement with biodiversity MEAs. As well as EU obligations, the highest priority was given to CBD, CITES and CMS. This has been realised in the size and level of delegations attending COPs –

---

74 This can bring problems for UK government when devolved administrations take policy positions contrary to the UK's international obligations, as was the case described in Box E when Welsh ministers took a policy decision not to provide legal protection to a Critically Endangered subspecies of goose.

hence there has been frequent attendance by ministers at CITES and CBD meetings but never for Ramsar, AEWA and others.

For a period, the UK withdrew from attending Bern Convention meetings since it was seen as functionally duplicating the Nature Directives. This was rapidly reversed after the decision to leave the EU, when the future significance of Bern came into sharper focus since its similar obligations to the Birds and Habitats Directives remain binding. Similarly, UK engagement with Ramsar has increased post-Brexit.

Overall, the UK's delivery of the Aichi Targets has either been poor (if one believes the government's own assessment – JNCC 2019b) or, according to independent assessment (RSPB 2020), extremely poor (see Table 3 above); so there is much to be done, and there are still many issues where a great deal could be improved. These include a failure to address weak coordination across government and between the component countries of the UK; a need to establish consistent UK responses to different MEAs dealing with the same issues; and inadequate engagement with NGOs and other sectors on many issues.

8 The impact of UK actions on an international scale

Historically, the UK has had a huge influence globally with respect to nature conservation and environmental protection. This has come through its colonial legacy; its scientific leadership reaching back to Victorian naturalists; diplomatic traditions; deep-rooted constitutional law; the dominance of the English language in scientific literature, policy-making, the internet and treaty negotiations, as described above; and the influence of citizen science through its NGO sector. The UK has powerfully influenced EU positions both within the context of the EU itself, and in developing EU positions for global negotiations. We consider below some of the many different ways that the UK supports environmental conservation, in support of MEA objectives, beyond its own territories.

Activities of non-governmental organisations

UK NGOs have had major impacts internationally. Some of the key contributors include the Wildfowl & Wetlands Trust (WWT); RSPB; the British Trust for Ornithology; Plantlife; Royal Botanic Gardens, Kew (RBG Kew); Whale and Dolphin Conservation; the Zoological Society of London (ZSL); the Royal Zoological Society of Scotland (RZSS); World Wide Fund for Nature-UK (WWF-UK); Fauna & Flora International (FFI); Wetlands International (formerly IWRB, which in 1998 moved its headquarters to the Netherlands) and many others. Some, such as RSPB and Plantlife, have played major roles in the development of partnerships of like-minded organisations around the world (respectively BirdLife International and Plantlife International). Broadly, the activities of UK NGOs have included:

- Active promotion of the multiple strands of science that need practically to come together to solve conservation problems – namely monitoring; prioritisation; diagnosis; intervention testing, and evaluation of outcomes of intervention (Gibbons *et al.* 2011);
- leadership in syntheses of information in support of international instruments (such as RSPB's continent-wide analyses of bird trends that underpinned defence of the EU Nature Directives – Donald *et al.* 2007; Sanderson *et al.* 2015 – see Box G);
- capacity-strengthening with equivalent national partner organisations (such as RSPB's long-term support to aid capacity development within other BirdLife International partners, including the development of statistically robust common-bird monitoring schemes in other European countries);
- delivery of direct intervention conservation projects (including captive breeding and re-establishment, seabird island restoration projects,[75] and landscape-scale restoration) by WWT and RSPB, ZSL, RZSS and several other zoos, and notably RBG Kew for plants;[76]
- provision of direct funding for conservation projects beyond the UK (especially WWF-UK and FFI);
- field research on conservation issues of international significance (for example, a range of botanical conservation projects undertaken by FFI, RBG Kew and Plantlife);
- advocacy with foreign governments related to activities damaging to nature conservation;
- fostering development of flyway-scale agreements and national policies for migratory waterbird and wetland conservation, supported by global monitoring programmes, such as the International Waterbird Census, and local capacity-building and resource mobilisation;
- purchase of land as nature reserves (or other direct support of specific protected areas), especially those that are part of international site networks (e.g. SPAs and/or Ramsar Sites [WWT, RSPB, Wildlife Trusts]); and
- influence of science, advocacy, and advice on continent-wide development of wider landscape measures such as EU agri-environment schemes.

Very often, UK NGOs undertake initial work overseas to develop projects or initiatives that are then subsequently taken forward with funding from local government.

---

75   Such as on Ascension and Henderson Islands and initiated on Gough Island in 2021.

76   Working in over 100 countries: www.kew.org/science/our-science/where-we-work

Hutan Harapan is one of the last remaining areas of dry lowland forest in Sumatra and is among the most threatened rainforests in the world. RSPB has been working with Indonesian conservation organisations to conserve and restore Hutan Harapan since 2007.

Scientific and research leadership

Overlapping significantly with the previous category is the very important role that UK universities and the wider scientific and technical community, including within NGOs (e.g. RSPB 2014), has played (and continues to play) internationally (Butchart *et al.* 2019). Such scientific work, for instance by the British Antarctic Survey, to name but one institution, has provided the bedrock for much international evidence-based decision-making. Good examples include strong scientific input to marine conservation in UK waters and more widely, and the huge role of UK atmospheric sciences in support of the IPCC. As just one species-related example, UK science has been critical to unravelling the threats to populations of albatrosses and influencing international response measures through ACAP and RFMOs. Such work is frequently undertaken collaboratively with institutions in other countries, particularly within the EU.

Direct financial support (aid)

The UK is a leading donor to overseas causes, spending £15.197bn on ODA in 2019, and since 2013, annually meeting the UN target of spending 0.7% of Gross National Income on ODA (DFID 2020).[77] That huge sum includes everything from disaster relief to cultural programmes; it is

---

77 It is one of five Development Assistance Committee donor countries to regularly meet this target. The others are Denmark, Sweden, Norway and Luxembourg. Only the USA and Germany contributed more than the UK in total. However, in November 2020 the UK government announced a temporary cut in foreign aid to 0.5% of national income, although committing to 'return to 0.7% when the fiscal situation allows' (www.gov.uk/government/speeches/official-development-assistance-foreign-secretarys-statement-november-2020).

impossible to isolate consistently the amount relating strictly to environmental issues, but it is likely to be very small.[78] Nevertheless, the UK government committed in June 2019 to ensuring that all development assistance is spent in ways that align with the Paris Climate Agreement, as part of a wider commitment to ensure that the UK achieves its target of net zero carbon emissions by 2050.

A further source of support is via the UK's considerable contributions to the Global Environment Facility (GEF), a funding mechanism created at the 1992 Rio Earth Summit.[79]

Financial and technical contributions to the work of the MEAs

The cost of UK annual support (assessed subscriptions or contributions) for MEAs is modest, by any yardstick. For CBD, CMS and four Agreements, as well as CITES, Ramsar and IPBES, it amounted to £2.001m in 2019/20.[80] This is a trivial amount in the context of the total UK government accounts but reflects the quite inadequate budgets established by COPs (see p. 31). Additionally, in that year contributions totalling £1.377m were made to the UNFCCC, the Montreal Protocol and the IPCC. Further contributions were made to OSPAR, RFMOs (via the EU), Antarctic treaties and more. This is critical funding for the operation of MEA Secretariats and implementation of certain actions. Under UN scales of allocations, the UK typically pays 4.5% of the costs of each global (UN) treaty. However, the UK contribution to regional MEAs can be considerably greater, reflecting the smaller number of Parties. For instance, it is 20% of ASCOBANS, 16% of ACAP and 12.6% of AEWA.

Funding for environmental activities by EU and UN is taken from those organisations' main budgets which is contributed from their Member States and other sources and is thus difficult to disaggregate to ultimate source.

Support for building international frameworks and institutions

The UK has historically been a strong diplomatic supporter of international institution-building; this is an important legacy of the UK's leading role in the post-war construction of a new world order. Interestingly, however, the UK

---

78 The five largest sectors for bilateral spend in 2019 (which totals £10.258m, or 67.5% of total UK ODA) were: 1. Humanitarian Aid – £1.536m (15% of total UK bilateral ODA); 2. Health – £1.431m (14%); 3. Multisector/Cross-cutting – £1.325m (12.9%); 4. Government and Civil Society – £1.313m (12.8%); 5. Economic Infrastructure and Services – £1.195m (11.7%). General Environmental Protection sits within Multisector/Cross-cutting and amounts to just 3.2% – £330,378 (a decrease from 11.1% – £577,701 in 2010) (Foreign, Commonwealth and Development Office 2020).

79 Since its creation, the GEF has disbursed US$20.5bn in grants and mobilised $112bn in co-financing for more than 4,800 environmental projects in 170 countries: www.thegef.org/about-us. GEF funds are 'replenished' periodically: the UK donated £210,000,000 in 2010 for the sixth replenishment, and £100,000,000 for the seventh replenishment (2019–2029).

80 A minimum value, as the UK often contributes funding for additional pieces of work arising from decisions and these are inconsistently accounted.

has not sponsored any recent global treaty,[81] thus also not hosting any of the more recently established Secretariat bodies[82] – most of which are in Bonn, Geneva, New York, Paris and Montreal. In the development of treaties, the UK contribution has been more technical, with major drafting input from a skilled cadre of international environmental lawyers within government and environmentalists both within and outside government.

Direct and indirect support of other countries

The provision of technical assistance from the UK in capacity-building or with other conservation programmes has been extensive. Undoubtedly the single most significant UK programme of support for conservation programmes overseas has been the Darwin Initiative,[83] announced by John Major at the Rio Earth Summit in 1992. Organisational support for the Initiative has changed through the years: it is currently run by a Defra team, with the Secretariat contracted out and advised by an independent expert committee. It has supported projects including institutional capacity strengthening; training; research; work to implement CBD, CMS, CITES, Ramsar, AEWA and other MEAs, as well as projects that generally promote environmental education or awareness. Since 1992 the UK government has granted over £177m to 1,220 Darwin projects in 159 countries.[84] The long-term impact of many of those projects has been considerable, as the project database demonstrates.[85]

81 Although, with the United Arab Emirates, the UK sponsored the development of the Raptors MoU under CMS.

82 Although the Secretariat of the IWC is based in Cambridge, and both the OSPAR Secretariat and the International Maritime Organisation office for the London Convention (on the Prevention of Marine Pollution by Dumping of Wastes and Other Matter) are in London. In former years, part of the Ramsar Convention's Secretariat (known then as the 'Bureau') was based at IWRB in Slimbridge.

83 Darwin Plus is a related programme that provides funding for projects in the UK Overseas Territories which are ineligible for funding under the main Darwin Initiative.

84 The initially pledged funding was £1m in 1993/94, with £2m and £3m respectively for the two subsequent years – less than the speculated annual budget of £10m suggested by officials in Rio de Janeiro (House of Commons Library 1993). Yet over the years since, Darwin Initiative funding – against all prospects – has been sustained.

85 www.darwininitiative.org.uk/project-search

9 Looking forward

Do we need (quite) so many treaties?

MEAs and the structures that they create serve to bring together people who are working on the same issue but based in different countries. Thus, as well as their primary decision-making role, they have a hugely important networking function. Each MEA can be seen as an international community of government experts, NGOs and supporting technical bodies, all with experience and expertise in relation to the treaty's objectives.

Although it would undoubtedly be tidier to merge all the treaties into one 'super-sized' MEA covering everything, it is hard to see how this would work in practical terms. Although mergers are a perennial topic of debate at international meetings, the wide range of issues involved is such that this is unlikely to occur in the short term. Moreover, the smaller MEAs with tighter remits are arguably better placed to point to successes on the ground, which are due to the focused and targeted attention they can bring to an issue. However, most MEAs mandate Secretariats to work more closely together to encourage 'synergy' (UNEP 2016), while a formal Liaison Group of Biodiversity-related Conventions periodically brings together the senior management of seven Conventions.[86] Other means of cooperation between

---

86 www.cbd.int/blg/

MEAs include elements such as Joint Work Programmes, formal cooperation MoUs, harmonised taxonomies and data standards.

Yet it is questionable how effective such synergistic working really is, since it seems to be human nature for small organisations such as Secretariats and governing bodies to be jealous of their 'turf'. Creation of even apparently straightforward administrative synergies within the CMS family of MEAs has proved to be intensely controversial. Further, lengthy debates on synergies in national reporting between MEAs have so far failed to lead to significant changes, given that reporting requirements for individual MEAs are typically relevant to their own specific needs, rather than reflecting shared issues.

Nonetheless, ensuring that decisions on issues of common concern are joined-up across different MEAs has been demonstrably more successful. A good example of how this works is presented by Cromie *et al.* (2011) in the case of development of guidance for dealing with Highly Pathogenic Avian Influenza (HPAI) H5N1 by AEWA, Ramsar and CMS. Close liaison between a small group of governmental and non-governmental experts led to the development of six complementary Resolutions by three MEAs and a significant package of accompanying technical guidance on best practice

Much formal guidance on the prevention of and response to outbreaks of HPAI H5N1 of Asian lineage was adopted by AEWA, Ramsar and CMS between 2005 and 2008. This significantly enhanced viral surveillance and epidemiological knowledge leading to greatly improved risk assessments.

responses. Critical to this was ensuring consistent messaging across these documents. Yet in the six-year period during which these three MEAs each agreed two Resolutions, CBD was still debating whether HPAI H5N1 was actually an 'emerging issue' – a not uncommon example of CBD's inability to respond rapidly.

There have also been examples where separate Conventions dealing with related issues have formally merged (such as the 1972 Oslo[87] and 1974 Paris[88] Conventions becoming OSPAR in 1992; the development by UNEP of a cross-cutting Strategic Approach to International Chemicals Management policy framework; or, as in the case of three Conventions [Basel, Rotterdam, Stockholm][89] related to hazardous chemicals management, the merging of Secretariats and holding back-to-back COPs). Of course, ultimately international frameworks only exist to address problems and, in theory, when those problems are 'solved' there should be no further need for their existence. Unfortunately, we seem far from that scenario at present.

The 'synergies' agenda is also relevant at the level of national imple-mentation, where concerns are often expressed that responsibilities for the different MEAs in many countries are divided in an unduly separate way between different departments, units of government or individual lead 'Focal Points', risking inconsistent or duplicated approaches to closely related issues. Hopes that National Biodiversity Strategies and Action Plans under the CBD might be a mechanism for promoting greater coordination at this level have not been well realised to date.

International environmental treaties in wider diplomacy

In post-conflict situations, diplomacy related to environmental issues can be valuable in (re)building relations between States: it is easier to start the talking with discussions on the needs of shared wildlife or natural resources than to address issues of military stockpiles (Carroll 1988). Some matters of high sensitivity, such as shared water resources, often remain intractable. While multiple formal treaties in this area aim to establish cooperation mechanisms concerning water, the reality is that these are frequently subject to reservations or other impediments to implementation.

Besides conflicts, international aid from the UK after natural disasters has been important in rebuilding the resilience and livelihoods of affected peoples. Within this, environmental issues have been significant, and increasingly are

---

87 Convention for the Prevention of Marine Pollution by Dumping from Ships and Aircraft.

88 Convention for the Prevention of Marine Pollution from Land-based Sources.

89 The Rotterdam Convention on the Prior Informed Consent Procedure for Certain Hazardous Chemicals and Pesticides in International Trade; the Basel Convention on the Control of Transboundary Movements of Hazardous Wastes and their Disposal; and the Stockholm Convention on Persistent Organic Pollutants.

linked to climate adaptation. For instance, Oxfam and Wetlands International ran a green coasts programme promoting mangrove restoration following the 2004 Indian Ocean tsunami.

Global target-setting

The setting of targets by COPs has increased in recent decades, typically in the context of tracking Strategic Plans (or, occasionally, 'Visions'). CBD's high-level targets established for 2010 and then again for 2020 (the Aichi Biodiversity Targets; CBD 2010b) have undoubtedly been influential in driving relevant national activity – albeit action that was inadequate in scope to deliver the targets in the UK (JNCC 2019b; RSPB 2020; Table 3).

Yet the political processes of setting these targets leave much to be desired. Fundamentally, it is not clear whether targets are firm commitments to be judged as being met, and whether, if achieved, this would solve the biodiversity crisis; or whether such targets are primarily a psycho-political device to move things on to a better place than we would have been in without them, and are thus essentially about setting a direction of travel.

Some have observed that transparently setting targets and then failing to achieve them (only to set new ones, which in turn need to become ever more ambitious due to past non-delivery) is in many ways a meaningless exercise that only serves to render the process less publicly credible each time it is undertaken. However, while States can indeed be criticised for national responses that are 'too little, too late', the reality is that there is no other diplomatic process that gets countries at least to debate the issues and – in theory – implement responses. Indeed, the last two or so years have seen CBD's 'Post-2020 Global Biodiversity Targets' subjected to intense international debate among both governments and NGOs, which certainly would not have occurred without this construct.

The role of international corporations

In the middle of the twentieth century, the centrality of government regulation with respect to nature conservation was clear – especially within international frameworks. Recent decades, however, have seen major growth in non-statutory structures that set standards for transnational corporations and promote other forms of best environmental practice. Many of the largest corporates now have their own environmental policies as an element of corporate social responsibility (Topping 2018). Although for some it is unclear the extent to which this amounts to 'greenwashing', at least for others, such individual company policies are genuinely significant. Some have established formal partnerships with MEAs (such as between the Danone Group and the Ramsar Convention) and with NGOs (such as between Shell and IUCN,

Earthwatch and Wetlands International). The World Business Council for Sustainable Development – formed in order to have input for the 1992 Rio Summit (Schmidheiny *et al.* 1992) – continues to provide a safe space for confidential dialogue between the senior management of many multinational corporations.

The International Standards Organisation has now established a wide range of standards relating to different aspects of environmental practice, and these have been valuable in developing good practice in many areas of endeavour.[90] In some areas, certification bodies such as the Marine and Forest Stewardship Councils can claim to have raised corporate environmental standards internationally through the use of market-based mechanisms.

The finance sector also has a growing role. For example, the International Finance Corporation's Environmental and Social Performance Standards define clients' responsibilities for managing their environmental and social risks, and these standards are being applied by the World Bank and others to major loans so as to evaluate the risk of serious environmental and social impacts.

It is beyond our scope to cover these issues here, but it is worth reflecting on the relative economic size of many of the largest transnational corporations in contrast to very many nations. While some Conventions are seeking engagement, it remains the case that the activities of most biodiversity MEAs remain, unfortunately, somewhat distant from these entities.

---

90 For instance ISO 14001, which represents the core set of standards used by organisations for designing and implementing an effective environmental management system.

10 Have MEAs made a difference?

A long view

If the outputs of the decadal global environmental summits or equivalent initiatives (1972, 1982, 1992, 2002, 2012) are compared, there appears to be a peak of principled ideals in integrative approaches in the early 1980s, coinciding with a peak in global support for intergovernmental multilateralism in general. Since then, both seem to have declined. At the same time, the length of Convention texts has increased concomitantly (compare the wise, visionary and simple text of Ramsar (e.g. Box B) with the pages of legalistic hedging in the CBD). It is inconceivable that a text like that of Ramsar would be adopted today.

This is disturbing in that, at a time of crisis (both in relation to climate, ecological emergencies and pandemics – all linked in whole or in part to humankind's damage to our environment), one might imagine that countries would band together more in common cause. However, in many instances we are seeing a retreat into nationalistic self-interest, with delegations to international biodiversity meetings now dominated by lawyers and foreign affairs officials at the expense of conservation experts. Such nationalistic retreat played out even more starkly in the initial responses to the COVID-19 pandemic, when it must now be clear to all that a concerted and shared international response was what was urgently needed – made even more imperative to ensure the equitable availability of vaccines to the poorest countries.

One of the crucial functions of MEAs is to provide the long view. Governments within democracies across the world are short-lived (in the sense that they are subject to re-election every few years), and typically new political parties come to the fore and existing priorities and timescales change.[91] In contrast, MEAs focus on longer timescales (and wider areas) and thus provide important perspectives separate from the vagaries of national political cycles.

MEAs are inherently 'slow burners' – typically taking a long time to negotiate, to come into force and then to establish their role and operations. Early COPs (i.e. first decades) are usually dominated by establishing structures, budgets and work programmes. It took 33 years from the first call for CMS by the Stockholm Conference to the adoption of a Strategic Plan by the established Convention (COP 8, 2005) outlining its operational priorities. And it is only now, in 2021, that the 1992 UNFCCC is having a meaningful influence on the national policies of multiple Parties.

Richard Lindsay (in litt.) memorably describes this:

'These treaties are like huge ocean-going ships of State. There is much activity on board to ensure that things run smoothly on a day-to-day basis while heading in a particular direction and destination. Any change in this direction and destination cannot be sudden or immediate otherwise the ship of State would overturn. Any change in direction is therefore mostly slow and ponderous,[92] but ultimately that altered destination may have profound implications for all on board. (On the other hand, if an iceberg is dead ahead, a sharp turn and consequent loss of crockery is preferable to the alternative.)'

MEAs have achieved much. Here are just a few of the things that would not be possible without them:

- National commitments to conserve over 2,400 wetland sites (an area of almost 254,563,791km² – greater than the size of Algeria), including high-altitude glaciers, freshwaters, intertidal areas and coral reefs, all of which support amazing biodiversity and help to meet human needs (Ramsar).
- Protection against over-exploitation through the regulation of international trade in 5,800 species of animals and 30,000 species of plants (CITES).
- Strict international protection for 181 globally threatened migratory species (defined as any that make predictable, cyclic movements across national boundaries), including albatrosses, gorillas and many marine mammals (CMS).

---

91 As do ministers: in the 23 years from 1997 to 2020 there have been 12 UK Environment Secretaries – with an average tenure of just two years.

92 That said, there are examples of MEAs acting swiftly in response to emergencies. Cromie *et al.* (2011) describe the rapid development of internationally endorsed policy guidance related to the emergence of HPAI H5N1 in the mid-2000s (see p. 62).

- A global regime to phase out the production and use of multiple ozone-depleting chemicals (Montreal Protocol).
- A European network of 27,852 protected areas covering 1,358,125km² – 18% of terrestrial and over 8% of marine surface areas of the EU and the UK – and helping to conserve multiple threatened species and habitats (EU Birds and Habitats Directives).
- An international regime for active promotion of the use of marine fisheries techniques that do not kill albatrosses and petrels (ACAP).
- Commitment from 80 States to phase out the use of toxic lead gunshot in wetlands, with 32 having fully (23) or partially (9) done so (AEWA).[93]

As with all human enterprises, however, MEAs are imperfect. For practitioners it is easy to be preoccupied with the imperfections and to push for good organisations to be even better. There are multiple ways in which MEAs and their Secretariats could improve their operations, and most seek to do this. Yet despite the deficiencies, if we started again, we would probably

Even sites that have the highest levels of 'protection' still face existential challenges. This coastal wetland at Yancheng, Jiangsu, in China, is a Ramsar Site and recently declared World Heritage Site. Its hugely important intertidal mudflats are threatened by, among other things, invasive *Spartina* grass, plastic pollution and wind farms.

93 In November 2020, the European Parliament voted to accept new regulations that will prohibit the use and possession of lead gunshot in wetlands across the EU. Unfortunately, the entry into force of this decision came just weeks too late to be binding on the UK. Whether the UK government decides to also adopt these regulations will be an important test case of its professed desire to maintain high environmental standards post-Brexit.

Street art in the city of Punta del Este, Uruguay, where an economy formerly based on long-line fishing is now driven by mass-market tourism. MEAs have particularly struggled to sustainably regulate the use of internationally shared marine resources of economic importance.

end up in a similar place, since structures for international cooperation in a geopolitically diverse world are part of the same geopolitics and diversity, with all their inherent messiness, tensions and unevenness.

The biggest issue remains not the MEAs themselves but their lack of national implementation. For example, analysis of the CMS African-Eurasian Migratory Landbird Action Plan found that *every single action* should already be delivered by other treaties (CMS 2014). Thus, the need for a Landbird Action Plan arises *entirely* from the failure to implement already agreed actions under other international frameworks.

And ultimately, nearly every internationally agreed environmental policy has the potential to be overridden nationally by the power politics of neoliberal economics when push comes to shove.

Yet despite these problems, and given the state of the planet, MEAs have never been so relevant or urgently needed. They are currently the only means we have of driving environmental improvements by states on an international scale. Global assessments certainly do manage to flag up the icebergs dead ahead – as in Richard Lindsay's metaphor. The question will be the extent to which MEAs can stimulate meaningful national change at the speed that is needed.

What of future directions?

In recent years, there has been increasing recognition of the importance of so-called non-state actors in environmental governance, both nationally and internationally. A good example is work towards achievement of climate targets by subnational entities such as cities, provinces or states, as well as by corporations. Such engagement is especially valuable where national governments may not be providing the leadership that they should. The role and importance of such non-state actors is likely to grow, not least given the economic size (and environmental impact) of many globalised, transnational corporations (Andonova & Hoffmann 2012; Green 2014; Bulkeley *et al.* 2014).

What would also undoubtedly help is greater public understanding of the work of MEAs, not least by including such international frameworks within education curricula. Commitments from governments worldwide are easy to make but hard to deliver. Greater public engagement could yield support for and, where necessary, scrutiny and challenge of objectives, which would certainly help in their delivery.

Overall, the budgets that States allocate to international environmental process are trivial compared to the immensity of the issues to be addressed and the size of national economies (p. 32). It is salutary to reflect on the funds allocated to MEAs (Figure 1) in the context of the budgets of most international corporates.

Much could come from greater 'mainstreaming' (to use environmental professionals' jargon) – incorporating beneficial environmental approaches within non-environmental policies and practices. To some extent this is happening,[94] but much, much too slowly. Positive conservation outcomes could (or should) come from the 'greening' of other agendas – especially industrial and economic processes. In this regard, the EU's recently announced Green Deal (European Commission 2019b) has huge potential.

The IPBES global assessment of biodiversity and ecosystems (IPBES 2019) highlights the need for 'transformative change' by society: business as usual with little green knobs on is no longer an option. The critical urgency required in responses is underscored by growing scientific understanding of tipping points and threshold effects, especially in the context of climate change. This need for change away from the status quo is, at last, fully recognised in the 'zero draft' of the proposed Post-2020 Global Biodiversity Targets (CBD 2020a).

The COVID-19 pandemic has yielded much discussion concerning various aspects of how society organises itself. The outcomes of associated debates and political decisions will undoubtedly have major implications for MEAs too, and will hopefully reinforce the role of international diplomacy in the management of shared environmental responsibilities and resources.

---

94 The 2006 Natural Environment and Rural Communities Act took a major step forward by imposing a legal duty on public authorities when 'exercising [their] functions, to have regard, so far as is consistent with the proper exercise of those functions, to the purpose of conserving biodiversity'. This still applies in England, while similar provisions apply elsewhere in the UK.

Final reflection on the role of individuals

As has hopefully been apparent throughout this book, and with an increasing focus on the need for leadership in conservation, the role of individuals in MEAs has been and remains critical, especially where those individuals (either within governments or NGOs) are active in multiple MEAs and so can cross-fertilise ideas and initiatives between frameworks. Margaret Mead's 1978 observation is just as pertinent and compelling today: 'Never doubt that a small group of thoughtful, committed citizens can change the world: indeed, it's the only thing that ever has.'

Appendix 1.
Main types of process for international cooperation

The European Union

The EU has a long-established and sophisticated framework of laws. These are initiated by the European Commission and agreed by Member States and the European Parliament. The most common form of EU legislation is the Directive (for example the 1979 Directive on the conservation of wild birds). In contrast to many forms of international forums, the EU has a strong compliance mechanism via the European Court of Justice (Box D).

International Conventions

Conventions are formal treaties/instruments that are legally binding on their Parties. The accession (or joining) to a Convention is a voluntary decision by a state which then becomes a Contracting Party to that Convention.[95]

Typically, each Convention has a Secretariat body which undertakes or coordinates relevant work between the regular meetings of the Conference of Parties (COP). The COP is the ultimate decision-making body,[96] and its meetings typically negotiate and agree Resolutions and Decisions – which outline desirable actions in relation to objectives, priorities and specific needs, and operational budgets (see p. 31). One of the main purposes of the COP

---

95 For more information on the processes by which a nation becomes a Contracting Party, see Chapter 5: International treaties: how they work.

96 Certain kinds of instrument have a Meeting of the Parties (MOP). There is no difference!

is to provide guidance on how Parties' legal obligations are to be interpreted and implemented. They also have an important role in adjusting the legal texts of treaties – the point being that these are not static instruments but evolve over time in response to new scientific information, emerging threats and other developments, with the result that Contracting Parties are sometimes required to adjust their domestic implementation measures. Good examples from among the conservation treaties are the changes to protected species' status (in light of data from monitoring) made by CITES, CMS and AEWA. Another especially interesting example is the Montreal Protocol, whose success is partially attributable to the progressive addition of obligations, acceleration of phase-outs of various ozone-depleting substances, and gradual increase in the number of substances covered by the treaty.

In addition to their aim to regulate state behaviour (and other administrative and legal/policy functions), Conventions stimulate and coordinate (typically via their Secretariat) programmes of work, projects, resource mobilisation activities and outreach initiatives, and provide support services to Parties.

Between COPs, a Standing Committee (or in the case of CBD, a similar body called the 'Subsidiary Body on Implementation') normally meets annually to supervise the work of the Secretariat and take necessary decisions. Typically, the larger Conventions have a scientific advisory body, for example the Scientific Council of CMS, or the Scientific and Technical Review Panel of the Ramsar Convention, which undertakes a defined body of work in support of the Convention and often also provides responsive advice to the Secretariat and Parties.

Agreements and Protocols (for example AEWA and ACAP), developed under the aegis of CMS, but legally separate from it, are functionally similar to Conventions, but typically these are restricted in scope either geographically or by species (for example covering African-Eurasian waterbird flyways in the case of AEWA).

Framework Conventions, such as the UNFCCC and the CMS (Boere 1991), establish high-level obligations for Parties, the main role of which is to create a framework (or negotiating mechanism) within which Parties can subsequently come together to negotiate more detailed agreements. Thus, the 1992 UNFCCC provided the mechanism by which States agreed the Kyoto Protocol in 1997, and subsequently the Paris Agreement in 2015. Both these subsequent treaties addressed climate issues in progressively greater detail (and with increasing negotiating belligerence, as it became ever more difficult to dodge the contentious issues).

Recent decades have seen a great growth in national engagement with multilateral environmental agreements. For example, while negotiations to conclude the Ramsar Convention in Iran in 1971 (above) were attended by delegates and observers from 23 countries and eight international organisations, the UN Conference on Environment and Development (Rio de Janeiro, Brazil) that concluded the 1992 CBD was attended by 177 countries, 87 international organisations and other entities, and many hundreds of national observer organisations.

There is also a Convention on Conventions! The 1969 Vienna Convention on the Law of Treaties is actually of huge significance for international lawyers, as it codifies comprehensive rules and guidelines as to how treaties are defined, drafted, amended and generally operate.

From a historical perspective, it is obvious that more recent MEAs have tended to become more comprehensive, and accordingly, have taken longer to negotiate because of growth in the understanding, interest and number of stakeholders (they are no longer issues with concern restricted largely to a small cadre of government officials). This is readily seen by comparing the simplicity of the 1971 Ramsar text (Box B) with that of any recent Convention.

Memoranda of Understanding (MoU), of which there are many under CMS (for example, on raptors, sharks and marine turtles), can be thought of as intermediate between Agreements (above) and Action Plans (below) in that, while they are legal instruments, they typically have few (if any) legal obligations (Galbraith *et al.* 2014). Some (but not all) have a budget and a Secretariat, and some allow non-state actors to be signatories and thus associate themselves with their aims. This can be useful in bringing some non-governmental energy.

Action Plans and non-binding instruments

There is a significant number of legally non-binding, but intergovernmentally agreed, frameworks for joint action (many of which are products of work by Conventions or the EU). These outline desirable actions in order to achieve a shared objective. An advantage is that they can be drafted and agreed relatively rapidly, but a significant disadvantage is that they typically have no allocated budget or Secretariat to drive work forward, nor any legal/regulatory 'teeth'.[97]

An example is the African-Eurasian Migratory Landbirds Action Plan adopted by CMS COP 11 in 2014, but which has since struggled to find traction with CMS Parties, who have repeatedly declined to approve the provision of resources from the CMS budget or to provide sufficient voluntary contributions to implement its actions. In this instance, BirdLife International has provided support for a part-time coordinator, and a few Parties (e.g. Switzerland, Ghana and the UK) have supported meetings. Such ad hoc support from the non-governmental sector is typical of how many Action Plans survive (just about) in the absence of adequate government financial support. Other examples include some MoUs and most CMS 'Programmes of Work'.

Other international structures

A wide range of other, non-legal international structures exists. An interesting example for waterbirds is the East Asian–Australasian Flyway Partnership,

An International Single-Species Action Plan for Greenland white-fronted geese (shown here in Hvanneyri, Iceland) was adopted by Parties to AEWA in 2012. It outlines necessary conservation actions for this subspecies, which occurs only in Greenland, Iceland, the UK and Ireland.

97 A useful comparison of the respective strengths and weaknesses of treaties versus non-binding instruments is provided by Galbraith *et al.* 2014 (pp. 29–31), who also stress another benefit of non-binding instruments in the flexibility to involve stakeholders from all sectors as equals. Such approaches support engagement with environmental NGOs in particular.

which brings together governments, Conventions, NGOs and corporates in a non-binding manner. While suffering some of the disadvantages of inadequate resourcing noted previously, it does allow those governments that are not party to particular Conventions to collaborate and benefit from guidance and other work done by Conventions and other binding agreements. The advantage has been to establish and give attention to large networks of important sites for migratory waterbirds, which include many sites that cannot, for various reasons,[98] be formally designated under the Ramsar Convention. Similar (although slightly different) frameworks exist also in the Americas, for instance the Western Hemisphere Shorebird Reserve Network, a regional network of sites of international importance for migratory birds.

Other international structures have been created by governments but are hard to categorise. The Global Environment Facility, IPCC and IPBES all have governmental membership with rules of accession, international governance arrangements and various types of governmental funding mechanisms. While not strictly MEAs, they provide crucial support for MEAs, as can certain structures of the UN, such as its Development and Environment Programmes.

On matters concerning the marine environment, governments collaborate within the frameworks of RFMOs to regulate specific (sometimes very wide-ranging) fisheries. These do not have a nature conservation objective, but the decisions that RFMOs take, for example in relation to bycatch mitigation measures, have hugely important consequences for reducing mortality of other species such as marine turtles, albatrosses and petrels.

---

98 In designating a Ramsar Site, the relevant Contracting Party assumes obligations on itself in regard to the 'wise use' of that wetland according to the terms of the Convention. Listing of a site within the EAA Flyway Network carries weaker, non-statutory obligations. Yet, as also for BirdLife International's Important Bird Areas, this serves the conservation of the site through awareness-raising and engagement with governmental structures locally, regionally and nationally.

Appendix 2.
How it works in practice: the evolution of international regimes to regulate whaling

The catastrophic consequences of overexploitation of the great whales over many centuries are well known and were an important trigger for 1970s environmentalism.[99] The story of international regulation to ensure sustainable harvesting highlights many of the classic challenges associated with the development of MEAs. These include:

- influence of vested and economic forces on international decision-making that should be based on science;
- serial avoidance of difficult decisions – sometimes for decades;
- inherent difficulties of agreeing radically changed policies in the light of new evidence (and interacting with weak and/or nationally partial chairmanship of international meetings);
- implications of a growth in number of Parties, bringing changed outlooks to debates;
- downstream consequences of inadequacies in the original legal text;
- consequences of a need for science-based management approaches but with a failure to fund the delivery of such advice;
- lack of compliance monitoring (detection of cheating);
- problems of enforcement.

---

99 Sources for the following account include Mackintosh (1965); Friends of the Earth (1974, 1978); Tønnessen & Johnsen (1982); Cherfas (1988); Heazle (2006); Morikawa (2009); Finlay (2011); Dorsey (2013); Zelco (2013); Ivashchenko & Clapham (2014, 2015); Clapham & Ivashchenko (2016); Fitzmaurice (2020).

At the beginning of the twentieth century the hunting to near, or actual, extinction of northern whale stocks was well attested. However, with the advent of new, more efficient technologies which allowed hunting first from land stations and then on the high seas with floating factories that had refrigeration, the need for regulation was clear and pressing. Vested interests in this activity were huge owing to the immense economic potential arising from the exploitation of whales as a source of meat and fats.

Such regulation at first emerged on the national level: for example, in 1921 the UK introduced licences and restrictions on whaling in its Antarctic dependencies. But from the start of modern whaling in the southern hemisphere, the signs were ominous for the economic sustainability of the industry (and also for the whales themselves, although this was apparently of little concern at the time).[100] With burgeoning pelagic whaling fleets in the 1920s operating beyond national waters, the concern for the long-term prospects of the industry grew in line with the escalating harvests (Figure 3) driven by the massive profits to be made. The 1920s were characterised by diplomatic dithering as the dimensions of an international agreement were explored. Should it regulate land-based stations as well as pelagic whaling (i.e. impinge on national sovereignty)? There were also issues of definition: such as whether permanently moored factory ships were 'land stations'; or whether regulation should be geographic through sanctuary areas, temporal through

Iceland's whale-catching fleet moored in Reykjavik Harbour alongside a vessel delivering whale safaris, 2005. The development of whale tourism is increasingly generating financial benefits to coastal States, and – as in Iceland – demonstrating economic alternatives to exploitation. The IWC has developed international good practice standards for boat-based whale watching.

---

100   Dorsey (2013), in his detailed review of international whaling diplomacy, notes that 'in all the recorded discussion in the 1930s, [there was just one] comment [concerning biological extinction of whales] that might compare to a modern environmentalist position.'

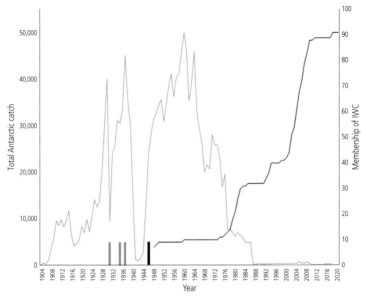

Figure 3. Progressive growth in membership of the ICRW (black line), showing periods of expansion in the 1970s, early 1990s and 2000s, set against changes in total Antarctic whale catches (blue line).[101] Red columns indicate three pre-Second World War international whaling conventions and the black bar indicates the 1946 ICRW.

closed seasons, or quota-based. And, critically, there was the question of how to prevent countries such as Japan from gaining commercial advantage by their refusal to join a collective regime of self-regulation – leading to competitive 'race to the bottom' attitudes from the whaling companies involved.

The eventual 1931 Convention for the Regulation of Whaling under the League of Nations at least established some basic restrictions, including a complete ban on the killing of 'right whales', including 'North-Cape whales, Greenland whales, southern right whales, Pacific right whales and southern pigmy right whales' (by then all commercially extinct anyway), and prohibition on taking females with dependent calves. It also required nations to record and report data on numbers taken. This Convention, which only came into effect in 1935, was followed by an elaborated but time-limited International Agreement for the Regulation of Whaling, sponsored by the UK, signed in 1937 by nine whaling nations (with additional Protocols for the 1938 and 1945 seasons), and which enlarged the scope of many of the same issues as well as newly establishing minimum-size thresholds for quarry species. While the introduction of such basic restrictions was welcome, attempting to constrain well-established and highly lucrative whaling enterprises on the high seas proved to be politically and practically difficult.

The loss of most whaling fleets during the Second World War gave a new opportunity to restrain the industry before it re-established. A new ICRW,

---

101   Data from Dorsey (2013) for the period 1904–1947; Heazle (2006) from 1948 to 1977 (corrected for falsified Soviet data to 1972); International Bureau of Whaling Statistics 1978–84; IWC since 1985; and from luna.pos.to/whale for minke (*Balaenoptera bonaerensis*) catches between 1962 and 2013.

sponsored by the USA, was signed by 15 whaling nations in 1946,[102] to 'provide for the proper conservation of whale stocks and thus make possible the orderly development of the whaling industry'. Crucially, ICRW established the IWC as a governance body charged to deliver its objectives in a proactive way. This Commission – addressing international resource management – was seen by the USA very much as a facet of the post-war 'Bretton Woods' international architecture (see p. 5) and as part of an explicit national policy of international fisheries management.

Although representing a major step forward, problems with the ICRW rapidly became apparent. The underlying reasons for the IWC's ineffectiveness during its first few decades were similar to those causing the failure of other international fisheries agreements of the same period – namely, policy objectives that massively outstripped the scientific understanding (and data) necessary to deliver them, and administrative procedures that were totally inadequate for the implementation of regulatory measures. Further, there was a complete lack of a collective ethos of shared responsibility with regard to its sustainable harvest objective, thus providing no meaningful resistance against the juggernauts of economic self-interest that dominated national positions during the post-war global food crisis.

Loopholes in the ICRW's already weak requirements allowed dissenting Parties, quite legally, to decline to implement regulations (such as individual quotas) with which they disagreed. Moreover, some Parties – notably the USSR and Japan – undertook extensive, state-sponsored, illegal pelagic whaling, killing not only strictly protected species but also taking whales without regard to age (i.e. including calves), sex and location, and falsifying data reported to the IWC.[103] While Parties were complicit in ignoring the obvious failure of the IWC's regulatory regimes,[104] the lack of any independent or international enforcement – and of any mechanisms to detect and respond to compliance – meant that such issues were always going to be hard to address. Cheating removed incentives for others to follow restrictive rules.

The drafters of the ICRW had seen an important need to offset the economic self-interest of the whaling industry by establishing a Scientific Committee

---

102 A Protocol signed in 1956 extended the ICRW's definition of a 'whale-catcher' to include helicopters (as well as ships) and is an example of the need for treaties to respond to technical and other developments.

103 Catch falsification involved overreporting during the legal season so that the international quota was quickly reached, leading to closure of the season and the departure of other whaling fleets, and then lack of reporting of what was subsequently illegally caught. One Soviet whaling inspector 'claimed to have witnessed the *Soviet Ukraine* [whaling fleet] catch 1,300 endangered and protected southern right whales in one season off Brazil, but he declined to report the infractions. Soviet whaling was, in his words, "extermination," and any killing done with[in] the rules was just 'a lucky coincidence.' Of the 234,000 whales killed by Soviet whalers between 1948 and 1927, only 140,000 were actually reported, he claimed, and more than 104,000 were caught in violation of IWC rules. On some expeditions, more than 50% of the take was illegal' (Dorsey 2013).

104 USSR's cheating was widely known and being discussed diplomatically at least from the early 1950s but never addressed within the IWC.

to provide independent advice to the Commission on the sustainability of catches. Yet for decades its activities were unfunded, and its advice typically ignored or deferred. Its maximum sustainable yield conceptual management model, pushed by the USA, turned out to be fundamentally flawed, being more of a political than scientific construct (although as the science was anyway being ignored this had little practical effect). The provision of independent science-based advice from the Scientific Committee to the Commission was further frustrated by Dutch input being determinedly in support of that country's national economic interests, while other scientists argued for higher quotas as being more 'politically realistic' – failing to understand the importance of decision-makers receiving independent scientific assessments.

Additionally, Parties could undertake unregulated 'scientific whaling', including on protected stocks, a procedure that has been used by Japan in particular.

However, from the mid-1970s, political dynamics within the IWC started to change as environmental NGOs encouraged non-whaling States to join the ICRW. This reflected growing public concern, especially with whaling becoming the poster child of 1970s environmentalism. There was also increased public recognition of the great whales as a part of the internationally shared heritage of all humanity and not just a resource to be exploited by a few economically self-interested countries. With IWC decisions requiring a three-quarters majority, the altered and enlarged composition of the commission (Figure 3) resulted in decisions now favouring 'the proper conservation of whale stocks' over 'the orderly development of the whaling industry' as previously. This finally resulted in the agreement of a moratorium on commercial whaling in 1982, which came into effect from the 1985/86 season and remains in place.[105]

The global 'Save the Whales' campaign was important in developing public environmental awareness during the 1970s. It generated significant political pressure on many governments regarding their policies towards whaling.

---

105   Although, between the start of the moratorium in 1985/6 and 2019/20, 57,939 whales have been taken under aboriginal capture and 'scientific whaling' provisions as reported by IWC. iwc.int/total-catches

However, from 2000 an increasing number of small developing countries (some of which are landlocked), in receipt of Japanese ODA, have joined the IWC and have consistently supported Japanese pro-whaling positions (Morikawa 2009; Dorsey 2013). This bloc has created a new oppositional, pro-whaling political dynamic within the IWC.

The inherent tension between the dual (arguably incompatible) objectives of the ICRW (*both* sustaining whales *and* sustaining whaling) lies at the heart of its failure to prevent the commercial extinction of most stocks of great whales since 1946, with regulations essentially coming too little and too late. Through the 1950s–1970s, the majority view within the IWC was dominated by national political needs to give priority to conservation of the economically important whaling industry[106] over that of the whales themselves.[107] State subsidy of their Antarctic pelagic industry by some countries (as implemented especially by the USSR) meant that whalers were significantly buffered from the commercial consequences of declining catches.

Attitudes to scientific uncertainty have been important and have changed. In the decades of overexploitation, uncertainty was used to justify excessive catches – it was impossible to demonstrate that there were as few whales left as the IWC's Scientific Committee claimed. More recently, an analogous approach to uncertainty is currently used to argue *against* reopening whaling, as it is not possible to be sure that there are as many whales as scientists claim.[108]

Several Parties have withdrawn from the IWC in response to its decisions, although some have subsequently rejoined[109] -- some in fact leaving and rejoining on more than one occasion. Most recently, Japan withdrew in 2019 in the aftermath of its case before the International Court of Justice (Clapham 2015).

Recent intense debates have focused on aboriginal whaling,[110] and the taxonomic scope of the ICRW, which the Convention does not define. This latter issue is especially significant in terms of whether the ICRW has a regulatory role for small whales and dolphins as well as baleen whales.

The ICRW remains in force and its fundamental weaknesses continue to be problematic in the context of annual decision-making on operational issues by

---

106   At its peak in 1955–56, the Antarctic whaling industry comprised 19 factory fleets with 257 catching boats.

107   For example, the complete protection of all Antarctic blue whale (*Balaenoptera musculus*) stocks was opposed by Japan, the USSR and the UK at the 1963 IWC meeting. However, 'in 1964, after [the UK] sold its last remaining factory ship to Japan … the British Commissioner proposed protecting the pygmy blue whale in addition to the larger blue whale, a significant change from the previous year' (Heazle 2006).

108   Heazle (2006) concluded his detailed review by 'proposing that political agendas are what set the parameters of policy making (and to a large degree of science itself); therefore, scientific uncertainty and the precautionary principle, in practice, often have been treated by many policy makers as little more than tools in the pursuit of their political objectives. In other words, it is not uncertainty itself that determines or influences policy making so much as how we choose to use it – and that is ultimately determined by political choices about what is or is not desirable.'

109   When Iceland rejoined, it did so with formal reservations on some issues.

110   There are frequently exemptions for indigenous subsistence activities in biodiversity conventions, but often these do not really work to protect indigenous livelihoods that involve both subsistence and commercial dimensions and depend on commercial markets to be viable. See Dorsey 2013.

the IWC. Notwithstanding the historical failure of the IWC to regulate catches sustainably from the 1940s to the 1970s, there is no doubt that without it many of the great whales would now certainly be biologically rather than just commercially extinct.

Has the ICRW been a success? Judged against the ICRW's two objectives, over its first four decades it sustained neither whales nor the whaling industry.[111] The introduction of a moratorium on commercial whaling from 1985/86 has since allowed some whale stocks to recover. While whaling on a biologically sustainable basis might well be possible now for a few stocks, the IWC's changed political make-up means that this is unlikely to occur. Thus, although arguably the ICRW is currently achieving one of its original objectives, that is, the conservation of stocks (or at least moving in that direction), it is not achieving the other, related to sustainable use.[112] However, many would contend that the two objectives are mutually exclusive due to the longevity and low reproductive rates of the great whales.

In the face of that failure, some whaling countries have either moved to create parallel international regulatory structures outside the provisions of the ICRW,[113] or are moving towards unilateral regulation of whaling – now seemingly to save national political 'face', in some instances, rather than for any particular economic advantage.[114]

IWC-66 meeting in Slovenia, 2016. The ICRW now has a much greater diversity and number of Contracting Parties than at its inception.

---

111   Branch *et al.* (2004) estimate that a population of 239,000 Antarctic blue whales a century ago was reduced to 360 by 1973. After 40 years of protection, numbers have increased to 1,700 (95% confidence interval 800–2,900 in 1996), just 0.7% (0.3–1.3%) of the pre-exploitation level.

112   Leaving to one side ethical and welfare considerations associated with whaling.

113   The North Atlantic Marine Mammal Commission was established in 1992 by the Faroe Islands, Greenland, Iceland and Norway.

114   Japan left the IWC on 30th June 2019 and announced it would resume commercial whaling in its territorial waters, no longer conducting 'scientific' whaling in Antarctic waters.

Abbreviations

Agreement on the Conservation of Albatrosses and Petrels	ACAP
Agreement on the Conservation of African-Eurasian Migratory Waterbirds	AEWA
Adaptive Harvest Management	AHM
Agreement on the Conservation of Small Cetaceans of the Baltic, North East Atlantic, Irish and North Seas	ASCOBANS
Convention on Biological Diversity	CBD
Convention on International Trade in Endangered Species of Wild Fauna and Flora	CITES
Convention on the Conservation of Migratory Species	CMS
Conference of the Parties	COP
Department for Environment, Food and Rural Affairs	Defra
European Court of Justice	ECJ
European Environment Agency	EEA
European Union	EU
Food and Agriculture Organization of the United Nations	FAO
Fauna & Flora International	FFI
Global Biodiversity Information Facility	GBIF
Global Biodiversity Outlook (CBD)	GBO
Global Environment Facility	GEF
Global Environment Outlook (UNEP)	GEO

Highly Pathogenic Avian Influenza	HPAI
International Court of Justice (UN)	ICJ
International Convention for the Regulation of Whaling	ICRW
Intergovernmental Science-Policy Platform on Biodiversity and Ecosystem Services	IPBES
Intergovernmental Panel on Climate Change	IPCC
International Union for the Conservation of Nature	IUCN
International Whaling Commission	IWC
International Wildfowl Research Bureau	IWRB
Joint Nature Conservation Committee	JNCC
L'Instrument Financier pour l'Environnement	LIFE
Millennium Development Goals	MDGs
Multilateral Environmental Agreement	MEA
Meeting of the Parties	MOP
Memorandum/a of Understanding	MoU
Marine Strategy Framework Directive (EU)	MSFD
Nature Conservancy Council	NCC
Non-governmental organisation	NGO
Official Development Assistance	ODA
Convention for the Protection of the Marine Environment of the North-East Atlantic	OSPAR
Memorandum of Understanding on the Conservation of Migratory Birds of Prey in Africa and Eurasia	Raptors MoU
Royal Botanic Gardens, Kew	RBG Kew
Regional Fisheries Management Organisations	RFMOs
Royal Society for the Protection of Birds	RSPB
Royal Zoological Society of Scotland	RZSS
Site of Special Scientific Interest	SSSI
Sustainable Development Goals (UN)	SDGs
Special Protection Area (EU Birds Directive)	SPA
United Nations	UN
UN Convention on the Law of the Seas	UNCLOS
UN Environment Assembly	UNEA
UN Environment Programme	UNEP
UN Educational, Scientific and Cultural Organization	UNESCO
UN Framework Convention on Climate Change	UNFCCC
Wildlife and Countryside Act, 1981	W&CA
World Heritage Convention	WHC
World Health Organization (UN)	WHO
World Wide Fund for Nature	WWF
Wildfowl & Wetlands Trust	WWT
Zoological Society of London	ZSL

References

Adams, R. 2008. Waterbirds, the 2010 biodiversity target and beyond: AEWA's contribution to global biodiversity governance. *Environmental Law* 38(1): 87–137.

Allan, J. I. (ed.) 2020. *The State of Global Environmental Governance 2019.* Earth Negotiations Bulletin, International Institute for Sustainable Development.

Andonova, L. B., & Hoffmann, M. J. 2012. From Rio to Rio and beyond: innovation in global environmental governance. *Journal of Environment and Development* 21: 57–61.

Bainbridge, I. P., Minns, D. W., Housden, S. D., & Lance, A. N. 1987. *Forestry in the Flows of Caithness and Sutherland.* Conservation Topic Paper 18. RSPB, Edinburgh & Sandy.

Birnie, P. W., & Boyle, A. E. 1992. *International Law and the Environment.* Oxford University Press, Oxford.

Black, R. 2016. Climate torture: UN's IPCC science panel must deliver clearer message. *Climate Home News,* 11th February 2016.

Boardman, R. 2006. *The International Politics of Bird Conservation: Biodiversity, Regionalism and Global Governance.* Edward Elgar, Cheltenham.

Bodansky, D. 2010. The development of international environmental law. *International Environmental Law-making and Diplomacy Review 2010*: 11–28.

Boere, G. C. 1991. The Bonn Convention and the conservation of migratory birds. In: Salathé, T. (ed.) *Conserving Migratory Birds,* pp. 345–360. ICBP Technical Publication No. 12. International Council for Bird Preservation, Cambridge.

Boere, G. C. 2010. *The history of the Agreement on the conservation of African-Eurasian migratory waterbirds. Its development and implementation in the period 1985–2000, within the broader context of waterbird and wetlands conservation.* UNEP/AEWA Secretariat, Bonn.

Bowman, M., Davies, P., & Goodwin, E. (eds) 2016. *Research Handbook on Biodiversity and Law.* Edward Elgar, Cheltenham.

Bowman, M., Davies. P., & Redgwell, C. 2010. *Lyster's International Wildlife Law.* Second edition. Cambridge University Press, Cambridge.

Branch, T. A., Matsuoka, K., & Miyashita, T. 2004. Evidence for increases in Antarctic Blue Whales based on Bayesian modelling. *Marine Mammal Science* 20(4): 726–754.

Brandt, W. 1980. *North–South: A Programme for Survival. Report of the Independent Commission on International Development Issues.* Pan Books, London.

Bulkeley, H., Andonova, L., Betsill, M. M., Compagnon, D., Hale, T., Hoffmann, M. J., Newell, P., Paterson, M., Roger, C., & Vandeveer, S. D. 2014. *Transnational climate change governance.* Cambridge University Press, Cambridge.

Butchart, S. H. M., Clements, A., & Gibbons, D. W. 2019. Conservation charities top citation charts. *Nature* 566: 182.

Carroll, J. E. (ed.) 1988. *International environmental diplomacy.* Cambridge University Press, Cambridge.

CBD. 2010a. Decision X/2. *The Strategic Plan for Biodiversity 2011–2020 and the Aichi Biodiversity Targets.* UNEP/CBD/COP/DEC/X/2.

CBD. 2010b. *Global Biodiversity Outlook 3.* CBD, Montreal.

CBD. 2014. *Global Biodiversity Outlook 4.* CBD, Montreal

CBD. 2018. Decision 14/37. Integrated programme of work and budget for the Convention and its Protocols. CBD/COP/DEC/14/37.

CBD. 2020a. *Update of the zero draft of the post-2020 Global Biodiversity Framework.* CBD/POST2020/PREP/2/1.

CBD. 2020b. *Global Biodiversity Outlook 5.* CBD, Montreal.

Chasek, P. S., Downie, D. L., & Brown, J. W. 2016. *Global Environmental Politics.* Seventh edition. Routledge, New York.

Cherfas, J. 1988. *The Hunting of the Whale.* Penguin, London.

Clapham, P. J. 2015. Japan's whaling following the International Court of Justice ruling: Brave New World – Or business as usual? *Marine Policy* 51: 238–241.

Clapham, P. J., & Ivashchenko, Y. V. 2016. Stretching the truth: length data highlight falsification of Japanese sperm whale catch statistics in the Southern Hemisphere. *Royal Society Open Science* 3: 160506.

CMS. 2014. *Conservation of migratory landbirds in the African-Eurasian region.* Annex 4 of UNEP/CMS/COP11/Doc.23.1.4/Rev.1.

Cooney, R. 2004. *The Precautionary Principle in biodiversity conservation and natural resource management: an issue paper for policy-makers, researchers and practitioners.* IUCN Policy & Global Change Series No. 2.

Cromie, R. L., Davidson, N. C., Galbraith, C. A., Hagemeijer, W., Horwitz, P., Lee, R., Mundkur, T., & Stroud, D. A. 2011. Responding to emerging challenges: multilateral environmental agreements and highly pathogenic avian influenza H5N1. *Journal of International Wildlife Law and Policy* 14: 206–242.

Dasmann, R. F. 1972. *Planet in peril? Man and the Biosphere Today.* UNESCO/Penguin Books, Harmondsworth.

de Klemm, C., & Shine, C. 1993. *Biological Diversity Conservation and the law: Legal mechanisms for conserving species and ecosystems.* IUCN Gland, Switzerland and Cambridge.

Defra. 2009. *United Kingdom Overseas Territories Biodiversity Strategy.* assets.publishing.service.gov.uk/government/uploads/system/uploads/attachment_data/file/69204/pb13335-uk-ot-strat-091201.pdf

Defra. 2018. *A Green Future: Our 25 Year Plan to Improve the Environment.* assets.publishing.service.gov.uk/government/uploads/system/uploads/attachment_data/file/693158/25-year-environment-plan.pdf

DeSombre, E. R. 2000. The experience of the Montreal Protocol: particularly remarkable, and remarkably particular. *UCLA Journal of Environmental Law and Policy* 19(1): 49–81.

DFID. 2020. *Statistics on international development. Final UK aid spend 2019.* Foreign, Commonwealth and Development Office, London.

Donald, P. F., Sanderson, F. J., Burfield, I. J., Bierman, S. M., Gregory, R. D., & Waliczky, Z. 2007. International conservation policy delivers benefits for birds in Europe. *Science* 317: 810–813.

Dorsey, K. 1998. *The Dawn of Conservation Diplomacy: U.S.-Canadian Wildlife Protection Treaties in the Progressive Era.* University of Washington Press, Seattle.

Dorsey, K. 2014. *Whales and Nations: Environmental Diplomacy on the High Seas.* University of Washington Press, Seattle.

Epstein, Y. 2013. The Habitats Directive and Bern Convention: synergy and dysfunction in public international and EU law. *Georgetown Environmental Law Review* 26(2): 139–174.

European Commission. 2011. *Our life insurance, our natural capital: An EU Biodiversity Strategy to 2020.* COM(2011) 244. European Commission, Brussels.

European Commission. 2019a. *The EU Environmental Implementation Review 2019. Country Report – Poland.* Brussels, 4.4.2019 SWD(2019), 128 final. European Commission, Brussels.

European Commission. 2019b. *The European Green Deal.* COM(2019) 640 final. European Commission, Brussels.

European Commission. 2020. *EU Biodiversity Strategy for 2030: Bringing nature back into our lives.* COM(2020) 380 final. European Commission, Brussels.

European Environment Agency. 2015. *European environment – state and outlook 2015: assessment of global megatrends.* EEA, Copenhagen.

European Environment Agency. 2020. *State of nature in the EU: Results from reporting under the nature directives 2013–2018.* EEA, Copenhagen.

FAO, & UNEP. 2020. *The State of the World's Forests (SOFO).* FAO & UNEP, Rome.

FAO. 2020. *The State of World Fisheries and Aquaculture (SOFIA).* FAO, Rome.

Ferrero-García, J. J. 2013. The International Convention for the Protection of Birds (1902): a missed opportunity for wildlife conservation? *Ardeola* 60(2): 385–396.

Finlay, C. 2011. *All the Fish in the Sea: Maximum Sustainable Yield and the Failure of Fisheries Management.* University of Chicago Press, Chicago.

Finlayson, C. M., & Gardner, R. C. 2018. Wetland law and policy: overview. In: Finlayson, C. M. *et al.* (eds) *The Wetland Book*, pp. 735–743. Springer, Dordrecht.

Fitzmaurice, M. 2020. International Convention for the Regulation of Whaling. Introductory Note. United Nations Audiovisual Library of International Law.

Fitzmaurice, M., Tanzi, A., & Papantoniou, A. (eds) 2017. *Elgar Encyclopedia of Environmental Law, Vol. V: Multilateral Environmental Treaties.* Edward Elgar Publishing, Cheltenham.

Freestone, D., & Ijlstra, T. (eds) 1990. The North Sea: perspectives on regional environmental co-operation. *Special issue of the International Journal of Estuarine and Coastal Law.*

Friends of the Earth. 1974. *Whale Campaign Manual 2.* Friends of the Earth, London.

Friends of the Earth. 1978. *Whale Manual '78.* Friends of the Earth, London.

Galbraith, C. A., Jones, T., Kirby, J., & Mundkur, T. 2014. *A Review of Migratory Bird Flyways and Priorities for Management.* CMS Technical Series Publication No. 27. UNEP/CMS Secretariat, Bonn.

Gibbons, D. W., Wilson, J. D., & Green, R. E. 2011. Using conservation science to solve conservation problems. *Journal of Applied Ecology* 48: 505–508.

Green, J. F. 2014. *Rethinking Private Authority: Agents and Entrepreneurs in Global Environmental Governance.* Princeton University Press, Princeton.

Greenland White-fronted Goose Study (in draft). A successful case of compliance under the African-Eurasian Waterbird Agreement: protection for Greenland White-fronted Geese.

Greenland Whitefronted Goose Study. 1986. Duich Moss: a minor administrative hitch… *Ecos* 7(2): 24–31.

Hayhow, D. B., *et al.* 2019. *The State of Nature 2019.* The State of Nature Partnership.

Heazle, M. 2006. *Scientific Uncertainty and the Politics of Whaling.* University of Washington Press, Seattle.

Hindle, E. 1964. International Wildfowl Research Bureau. In: Hoffmann, L. (ed.) *Project Mar. The conservation and management of temperate marshes, bogs and other wetlands. Proceedings of the Mar Conference organised by IUCN, ICBP and IWRB at Les Saintes-Maries-de-la-Mer, November 12–16 1962*, pp. 461–468. IUCN Publications new series No. 3, Morges.

HMSO. 2020a. *Welsh Statutory Instrument 2020 No. 272 (W. 64). The Wildlife and Countryside Act 1981 (Variation of Schedule 2) (Wales) Order 2020.*

HMSO. 2020b. *Statutory Instrument 2020 No. 245. The Wildlife and Countryside Act 1981 (Variation of Schedule 2) (England) Order 2020.*

Hoffmann, L. 1964. *Project Mar. The conservation and management of temperate marshes, bogs and other wetlands. Proceedings of the Mar Conference organised by IUCN, ICBP and IWRB at Les Saintes-Maries-de-la-Mer, November 12–16 1962.* IUCN Publications new series No. 3, Morges.

Holdgate, M. 1999. *The Green Web: A Union for World Conservation.* Earthscan Publications, London.

Housden, S. 2015. Fighting for wildlife – from the inside. In: *Nature's Conscience: The Life and Legacy of Derek Ratcliffe*, pp. 359–370. Langford Press, Norfolk.

House of Commons Environment, Transport and Regional Affairs Committee. 1999. *Sixteenth Report. Multilateral Environmental Agreements. Vol. 1. Report and Proceedings of the Committee.* The Stationary Office, London.

House of Commons Library. 1993. *The Earth Summit: one year on.* Research Report 93/71. House of Commons, London.

IPBES. 2019. *Summary for policymakers of the global assessment report on biodiversity and ecosystem services of the Intergovernmental Science-Policy Platform on Biodiversity and Ecosystem Services.* Díaz, S., *et al.* (eds). IPBES secretariat, Bonn.

IPCC. 2018. Special Report: Global Warming of 1.5°C. www.ipcc.ch/sr15

IUCN. 2007. *Guidelines for applying the precautionary principle to biodiversity conservation and natural resources management.* IUCN, Gland.

IUCN, UNEP, & WWF. 1980. *World Conservation Strategy: Living Resource Conservation for Sustainable Development.* IUCN, Gland.

IUCN, UNEP, & WWF. 1991. *Caring for the Earth: A Strategy for Sustainable Living.* IUCN, Gland.

Ivashchenko, Y. V., & Clapham, P. J. 2014. Too much is never enough: The cautionary tale of Soviet illegal whaling. *Marine Fisheries Review* 76(1–2): 1–21.

Ivashchenko, Y. V., & Clapham, P. J. 2015. What's the catch? Validity of whaling data for Japanese catches of sperm whales in the North Pacific. *Royal Society Open Science* 2: 150177.

JNCC. 2009. *Global biodiversity mechanisms: a thematic review of recent developments and future evidence needs? Summary of Conference Proceedings.* www.yumpu.com/en/document/read/26839661/summary-of-conference-proceedings-jncc-defra

JNCC. 2019a. *11th Report by the United Kingdom under Article 12 on the implementation of the Directive on the conservation of wild birds (2009/147/EC) from January 2013 to December 2018.* JNCC, Peterborough.

JNCC. 2019b. *Sixth National Report to the United Nations Convention on Biological Diversity: United Kingdom of Great Britain and Northern Ireland.* JNCC, Peterborough.

King, M. 2020. Comment: What legacy for Gove? *British Wildlife* 31(3): 189–193.

Kuijken, E. 2006. A short history of waterbird conservation. In: Boere, G. C., Galbraith C. A., & Stroud, D. A. (eds) *Waterbirds Around the World*, pp. 52–59. The Stationery Office, Edinburgh.

Kuokkanen, T., Couzens, E., Honkonen, T., & Lewis, M. (eds) 2016. *International environmental law-making and diplomacy: insights and overviews*. Routledge, London.

Leggett, J. K. 2000. *The Carbon War: Global Warming and the End of the Oil Era*. Penguin, London.

Lewis, M. 2016. AEWA at Twenty: an appraisal of the African-Eurasian Waterbird Agreement and its unique place in international environmental law. *Journal of International Wildlife Law* 19(1): 22–61.

Lewis, M. 2019. *An Appraisal of the African-Eurasian Waterbird Agreement and its Role in the Conservation and Management of Migratory Birds at Flyway-level*. PhD thesis, Tilburg University, The Netherlands.

Lindsay, R. A., Charman, D. J., Everingham, F., O'Reilly, R. M., Palmer, M. A., Rowell, T. A., & Stroud, D. A. 1988. *The Flow Country: The Peatlands of Caithness and Sutherland*. Nature Conservancy Council, Peterborough.

Mace, G. M., Collar, N. J., Gaston, K. J., Hilton-Taylor, C., Akçakaya, H. R., Leader-Williams, N., Milner-Gulland, E. J., & Stuart, S. 2008. Quantification of extinction risk: IUCN's system for classifying threatened species. *Conservation Biology* 22(6): 1424–1442.

Mackintosh, N. A. 1965. *The Stocks of Whales*. Fishing News (Books) Ltd, London.

Maes, J. *et al.* 2020. *Mapping and Assessment of Ecosystems and their Services: An EU ecosystem assessment*. Publications Office of the European Union, Luxembourg. publications.jrc.ec.europa.eu/repository/handle/JRC120383

Matthews, G. V. T. 1993. *The Ramsar Convention on wetlands: its history and development*. Ramsar Convention Bureau, Switzerland.

Millennium Ecosystem Assessment. 2005. *Ecosystems and Human Well-being: Synthesis*. Island Press, Washington DC.

Mitchell, I., Newton, S. F., Ratcliffe, N., & Dunn, T. E. 2004. *Seabird Populations of Britain and Ireland*. T., & A.D. Poyser, London.

Mitchell, R. B. 2010. *International Politics and the Environment*. Sage Publications, London.

Mitchell, R. B. 2016. International Environmental Agreements (IEA) Database Project. University of Oregon. iea.uoregon.edu

Montanarella, L., Scholes, R., & Brainich, A. (eds) 2018. *The IPBES assessment report on land degradation and restoration*. Secretariat of the Intergovernmental Science-Policy Platform on Biodiversity and Ecosystem Services. IPBES, Bonn. doi.org/10.5281/zenodo.3237392

Morikawa, J. 2009. *Whaling in Japan: Power, Politics, and Diplomacy*. Columbia University Press, New York.

Nicholson, M. 1967. *The System: The Misgovernment of Modern Britain*. Hodder and Stoughton, London.

Nicholson, M. 1970. *The Environmental Revolution*. Penguin Books, Harmondsworth.

Oldfield, S., Procter, D., & Fleming, V. 1999. *Biodiversity: the UK Overseas Territories*. JNCC, Peterborough.

Olney, P. J. S. 1965. *Project Mar for the conservation and management of temperate wetlands. Volume 2. List of European and North African wetlands of international importance*. IUCN Publications new series No. 5. IUCN, Morges.

Pachauri, R. K., & Meyer, L. A. 2014. *Climate Change 2014: Synthesis Report. Contribution of Working Groups I, II and III to the Fifth Assessment Report of the Intergovernmental Panel on Climate Change*. IPCC, Geneva.

Paterson, M., Humphreys, D., & Pettiford, L. 2003. Conceptualizing global environmental governance: from interstate regimes to counter-hegemonic struggles. *Global Environmental Politics* 3(2): 1–10.

Piersma, T. 1986. Breeding waders in Europe: a review of population size estimates and a bibliography of information sources. *Wader Study Group Bulletin* 48, supplement.

Potts, S. G., Imperatriz-Fonseca, V. L., & Ngo, H. T. (eds) 2016. *The assessment report of the Intergovernmental Science-Policy Platform on Biodiversity and Ecosystem Services on pollinators, pollination and food production*. Secretariat of the Intergovernmental Science-Policy Platform on Biodiversity and Ecosystem Services. IPBES, Bonn. doi.org/10.5281/zenodo.3402856

Pritchard, D. E. 1997. European law on nature conservation sites and its impact in the UK. *RSPB Conservation Review* 11: 39–43.

Pritchard, D. E. 2016a. Wise use concept of the Ramsar Convention. In: Finlayson, M., & Davidson, N. (eds) *The Wetland Book*, pp. 477–480. Springer, Dordrecht.

Pritchard, D. E. 2016b. Ecological character concept of the Ramsar Convention. In: Finlayson, M., & Davidson, N. (eds) *The Wetland Book*, pp. 473–476. Springer, Dordrecht.

Ramsar Convention on Wetlands 2018. *Global Wetland Outlook: State of the World's Wetlands and their Services to People*. Ramsar Convention Secretariat. Gland, Switzerland.

Ratcliffe, D. 1968. An ecological account of Atlantic bryophytes in the British Isles. *New Phytologist* 67: 365–439.

Rogers, R. 1983. *Lead poison*. New Statesman Report 7. London.

RSPB. 2014. *RSPB Centre for Conservation Science*. RSPB, Sandy.

RSPB. 2020. *A Lost Decade for Nature*. RSPB, Sandy.

Sand, P. H. 2013. Enforcing CITES: The rise and fall of trade sanctions. *Review of European Community & International Environmental Law* 22(3): 251–263.

Sanderson, F. J., Pople, R. G., Ieronymidou, C., Burfield, I. J., Gregory, R. D., Willis, S. G., Howard, C., Stephens, P. A., Beresford, A. E., & Donald, P. F. 2015. Assessing the performance of EU nature legislation in protecting target bird species in an era of climate change. *Conservation Letters* 9(3): 172–180.

Schmidheiny, S. 1992. *Changing Course: A Global Business Perspective on Development and the Environment.* MIT Press, Boston.

Schmidt, P. R. 2006. North American Flyway Management: a century of experience in the United States. In: Boere, G. C., Galbraith, C. A., & Stroud, D. A. (eds) *Waterbirds Around the World,* pp. 60–62. The Stationery Office, Edinburgh.

Scottish Government 2013. *2020 Challenge for Scotland's Biodiversity.* Scottish Government.

Sheail, J. 1998. *Nature Conservation in Britain: The Formative Years.* The Stationery Office, London.

Sheila McKechnie Foundation 2018. *The Chilling Reality: How the Lobbying Act is affecting charity and voluntary sector campaigning in the UK.* Sheila McKechnie Foundation, London.

Sissenwine, M. P., & Rosenberg, A. A. 1993. Marine fisheries at a critical juncture. *Fisheries* 18(10): 6–14.

Stoneman, R. 2016. The IUCN-UK Peatland Programme and the Yorkshire Peat Partnership. In: *Proceedings of 15th International Peat Congress,* pp 407–409.

Stroud, D. A. 1985. The case of Duich Moss. *Ecos* 6(1): 46–48.

Stroud, D. A. 2015. Regulation of some sources of lead poisoning: a brief review. In: Delahay, R. J., & Spray, C. J. (eds) *Proceedings of the Oxford Lead Symposium. Lead ammunition: understanding and minimising the risks to human and environmental health,* pp. 8–26. The University of Oxford, Oxford.

Stroud, D. A., Pienkowski, M. W., & Mudge, G. P. 1990. *Protecting internationally important bird sites: a review of the network of EC Special Protection Areas in Great Britain.* Nature Conservancy Council, Peterborough.

Stroud, D. A., Reed, T. M., Pienkowski, M. W., & Lindsay, R. A. 1987. *Birds, Bogs and Forestry: The Peatlands of Caithness and Sutherland.* Nature Conservancy Council, Peterborough.

Stroud, D. A., Reed, T. M., Pienkowski, M. W., & Lindsay, R. A. 2015. The Flow Country: battles fought, war won, organisation lost. In: Thompson, D., Birks, H., & Birks, J. (eds) *Nature's Conscience: The Life and Legacy of Derek Ratcliffe,* pp. 401–439. Langford Press, Norfolk.

Tompkins, S. C. 1986. *The Theft of the Hills: Afforestation in Scotland.* Ramblers Association, London.

Tønnessen, J. N., & Johnsen, A. O. 1982. *The History of Modern Whaling.* Hurst and Co., London.

Topping, C. 2018. Corporate social responsibility: do companies care about biodiversity? *British Wildlife* 29(3): 197–203.

Trouwborst, A., *et al.* 2017. International wildlife law: understanding and enhancing its role in conservation. *BioScience* 67(9): 784–790. doi:10.1093/biosci/bix086

UN Environment. 2019. *Global Environment Outlook – GEO-6: Healthy Planet, Healthy People.* United Nations Environment Programme, Nairobi. doi: 10.1017/9781108627146.

UN General Assembly. 2015. *Transforming our World: The 2030 Agenda for Sustainable Development.* A/RES/70/1.

UNEP. 2016. *Enhancing cooperation among the seven biodiversity related agreements and conventions at the national level using national biodiversity strategies and action plans.* United Nations Environment Programme, Nairobi.

UNESCO, UN-Water. 2020. *United Nations World Water Development Report 2020: Water and Climate Change.* UNESCO, Paris.

United Nations Convention to Combat Desertification. 2017. *The Global Land Outlook, first edition.* UNCCD, Bonn.

Wetlands International. 2012. *Waterbird Population Estimates, Fifth Edition.* Summary Report. Wetlands International, Wageningen.

Williams, G., Pullan, D., Dickie, I., Huggett, D., & Mitchell, H. 2005. *The European Birds Directive – safeguarding special places for people and wildlife.* RSPB, Sandy.

Wilson, D. 1983. *The Lead Scandal: The Fight to Save Children from Damage by Lead in Petrol.* Heinemann Educational Books, London.

Wilson, D. 1984. *Pressure: The A to Z of Campaigning in Britain.* Heinemann Educational Books, London.

Wilson, J. D., Anderson, R., Bailet, S., Chetcuti, J., Cowie, N. R., Hancock, M. H., Quine, C. P., Russell, N., Stephen, L., & Thompson, D. B. A. 2014. Modelling edge effects of mature forest plantations on peatland waders informs landscape-scale conservation. *Journal of Applied Ecology* 51: 204–213.

Wolf, A. 1997. *Quotas in International Environmental Agreements.* Earthscan, London.

World Commission on Environment and Development. 1987. *Our Common Future.* UN/Oxford University Press, Oxford.

Zelco, F. 2013. *Make It a Green Peace! The Rise of Counterculture Environmentalism.* Oxford University Press, Oxford.

Further reading and resources

Multilateral environmental agreements

Mitchell (2016) provides an online database of MEAs. The International Institute for Sustainable Development's *Earth Negotiations Bulletin* (enb.iisd.org/enb/) gives an invaluable archive of historical reportage on many international treaties and processes, while the UN's InforMEA (www.informea.org/en) is a means of exploring much information on MEAs. Although dated in respect to detail, the 1999 report of the House of Commons Environment, Transport and Regional Affairs Committee review of UK's engagement with, and implementation of, MEAs is still highly relevant.

International law

Both de Klemm & Shine (1993) and Birnie & Boyle (1992), although not including recent developments, are excellent, thorough summaries of the legal background and history to international environmental treaties. More recent good summaries include Fitzmaurice *et al.* (2017), Bowman *et al.* (2010, 2016) and Kuokkanen *et al.* (2016). Trouwborst *et al.* (2017) present an accessible recent review of the relevance of international instruments specifically to nature conservation. Chasek *et al.* (2016) detail the development of major environmental regimes through case studies on climate change, toxic chemicals and biodiversity loss.

Making treaties

Matthews (1993) presents a very readable account of the historical development of the Ramsar Convention and its first 25 years of implementation. Boere (2010) similarly gives an accessible and highly illustrated history of the genesis and negotiations leading up to the finalisation of AEWA and its first MOP. The AEWA story from there is taken up by Adams (2008) and then Lewis (2016, 2019). Bodansky (2010) usefully reviews the development of international environmental law. Leggett (2000) presents a gripping insider's view of attempts by vested interests to weaken climate change processes in the 1990s.

Following MEAs

The *Earth Negotiations Bulletin* provides a range of free information materials as well as daily reporting from selected MEA events (enb.iisd.org/about/earth-negotiations-bulletin).

Setting international contexts: sharing data and information

Fundamental to tracking targets and understanding the current state of the environment is access to relevant and up-to-date biodiversity data. Networks such as the UK's National Biodiversity Network, the Arctic Data Centre and the Global Biodiversity Information Facility (GBIF) are examples of organisations facilitating data-sharing at national, regional and global scales, respectively. In an international context, GBIF not only facilitates access to over 1.6 billion species occurrence records but also cultivates and supports a global community of practice that promotes the flow of open-access biodiversity data through regional and thematic training programmes (www.gbif.org/training).

European Union

A huge amount of information about Europe's environment, including multiple thematic assessments, is available on the EEA's website (www.eea.europa.eu). The outputs of reporting under the EU Birds and Habitats Directives are available on the portal of the European Environment Information and Observation Network (Eionet), which is a partnership network of the EEA and its 38 member and cooperating countries.

International organisations and how they work

Holdgate's (1999) memoir on the development and history of the IUCN gives extensive information on the evolving international context for environmental conservation throughout the twentieth century, while the chaotic and depressing development of the IWC is thoroughly documented by Tønnessen & Johnsen (1982), and well synthesised by Heazle (2006) and Dorsey (2013).

Illustration credits

Images not listed here are credited to David Stroud.

4 © Reproduced with permission from *Project Mar: the conservation and management of temperate marshes, bogs and other wetlands = Projet Mar: conservation et aménagement des marécages, tourbières et autres milieux humides en zone tempérée (Volume 2)*, compiled by P. J. S. Olney, 1965, portals.iucn.org/library/node/6209; **5** © Norman Russell/rspb-images.com; **6** © 2019, Intergovernmental Science-Policy Platform on Biodiversity and Ecosystem Services (IPBES); **8** © EEA, Copenhagen, 2015; **10** © Sacha Dench/WWT; **12** © Cairngorms Connect/scotlandbigpicture.com; **13** © UNEP/AEWA Secretariat; **18** © Graham Howie/WWT; **24** © Royal Netherlands Institute for Sea Research; **25** © UN Photo/Yutaka Nagata (material obtained on 10th February 2021 from the website of the United Nations Audiovisual Library of International Law, located at www.un.org/law/avl); **28** © IISD/END, Kiara Worth enb.iisd.org/cites/cop17/3oct.html; **29** © IISD/END, Natalia Mroz enb.iisd.org/ozone/mop31/8nov.html; **29** © IISD/ENB, Dan Birchall enb.iisd.org/ramsar/cop11/13jul.html; **30** © IISD/ENB, Francis Dejon enb.iisd.org/cites/cop16/6mar.html; **32** © Graeme MacKay 'Collapsing biodiversity is another looming wave of destruction'/Artizans.com; **39** © IISD/ENB, Francis Dejon enb.iisd.org/biodiv/wgpa/17june.html; **47** © H McFarlane/Fidra; **48** © WWF/Birdlife/FOE/EEB, Friends of the Earth Europe; **58** © Steve Rowland/rspb-images.com; **62** © WWT; **68** © Taej Mundkur; **74** © Reproduced with permission from Wetlands International: Carp, E. (ed.) 1972. *Proceedings of the International Conference on the Conservation of wetlands and waterfowl*. Ramsar, Iran, 30 January–3 February 1971. International Wildfowl Research Bureau, Slimbridge; **75** © Chris Wilson; **81** © Friends of the Earth; **83** © IISD/ENB enb.iisd.org/iwc/66/28oct.html

About the authors

The authors bring a huge wealth of expertise from their past and current positions within both statutory and non-government nature conservation organisations (Joint Nature Conservation Committee, Royal Society for the Protection of Birds, BirdLife International; BirdLife South Africa; National Biodiversity Network; Scottish Wildlife Trust; BirdWatch Ireland; Wildfowl & Wetlands Trust; Scottish Environment Protection Agency; Environment Agency); international organisations (Wetlands International); and academia (Universities of Dundee, Tilburg [Netherlands], Charles Sturt University [Australia] and KwaZulu-Natal [South Africa]) – although the views they bring to the task are their own. They have also worked in multiple capacities with, and for, international organisations including the European Union; Biodiversity Convention; Ramsar Convention on Wetlands; Convention on Migratory Species; Convention on the Conservation of European Wildlife and Natural Habitats; African-Eurasian Waterbirds Agreement; Agreement on the Conservation of Albatrosses and Petrels; OSPAR; International Council for the Exploration of the Sea (ICES); and many others.

The capacities through which they have engaged with international conservation have included as representatives of governments, and of national and international non-government organisations; through involvement in Convention scientific advisory bodies; as lobbyists; and through Secretariat advisory support; as well as close involvement with a range of national governments in the challenging and important task of implementing international obligations nationally. This collective experience provides rounded views on the critical importance of international treaties for nature conservation.

Acknowledgements

The authors would like to thank Vin Fleming, Kate Harris, Richard Lindsay and Kate Neville, who significantly improved the text with very helpful and perceptive comments drawn from their long international experience.